OPTICAL PUZZLES

METRO BOOKS
NEW YORK

METRO BOOKS
New York

An Imprint of Sterling Publishing
387 Park Avenue South
New York, NY 10016

METRO BOOKS and the distinctive Metro Books logo are trademarks of
Sterling Publishing Co., Inc.

© 2012 by Arcturus Publishing Limited/Gianni A. Sarcone and Marie-Jo Waeber

This 2012 edition published by Metro Books, by arrangement with
Arcturus Publishing Limited.

ISBN: 978-1-4351-4342-5

For information about custom editions, special sales, and premium and corporate
purchases, please contact Sterling Special Sales at 800-805-5489 or
specialsales@sterlingpublishing.com.

Manufactured in Singapore

1 3 5 7 9 10 8 6 4 2

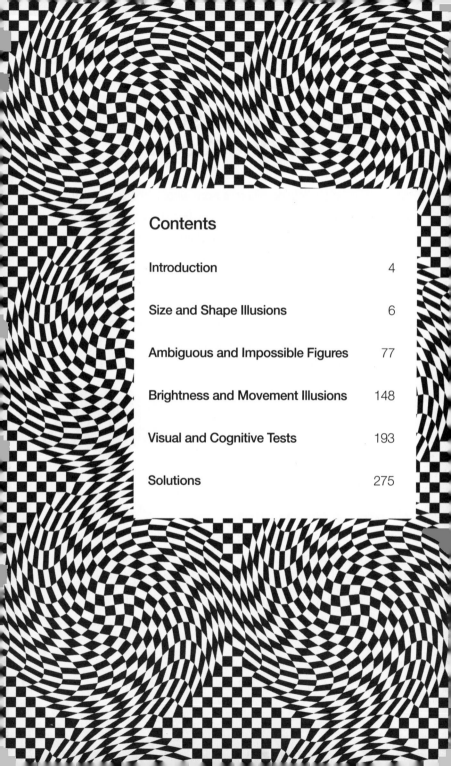

Contents

To see or not to see, that is the question . . .

When you see something different from what is there in reality, you are experiencing an optical illusion. But did you know that visual illusions have existed since the dawn of mankind?

Optical illusions appeared along with the birth of painting: look at the vigorous and precise strokes portraying a galloping wild boar in a cave near Altamira, Spain. The prehistoric artist created the illusion of movement by using a dynamic blur, as seen in some modern photographs: the two pairs of legs painted with lighter colors suggest the boar was running so fast that the artist 'perceived' more legs than the actual four. Not only was the portrayal of motion the purpose of this painting, it may also have been the expression of a very early curiosity from the artist as to why he or she was seeing more

The galloping eight-legged boar of Altamira

legs than the number that were known to be there. However, persistence of vision and the blurring effect of after-images would actually not be understood for several millennia!

From prehistory to the present day, optical illusions have helped us to reflect upon the reality of what is seen and to understand a little better some of the errors of perception we make. Over the years, scientists have been studying and utilizing optical illusions to gain insights into how our brain interprets information and build a representation of the surroundings.

Yet illusions can also be employed as educational or improvement tools. In fact, stepping outside your comfort zone and thinking in ways that are both creative and challenging to your visual perception is a kind of exercise that may increase your brain flexibility. Just as going to the gym keeps you physically fit, completing visual puzzles will keep you mentally fit.

This entertaining book, divided into four sections, will train your eyes and your mind to avoid most common visual trickeries. In the first section you will hone your judgment of size and shape; the second section dives into illusions involving impossible and ambiguous figures; the third deals with brightness and moving patterns; and, finally, in section four, you will assess and improve your visual-spatial intelligence — the ability to mentally manipulate three-dimensional objects, or to discriminate objects from the background — with original tests created or adapted by the authors.

Dear reader, enjoy being deceived and don't be afraid to make a lot of errors, because they are just fruitful stages on the road of knowledge.

Gianni A. Sarcone and **Marie-Jo Waeber,**
researchers and artists.

SIZE AND SHAPE ILLUSIONS

Tolansky Curvature

Are the three arc segments A, B, and C identical in curvature?

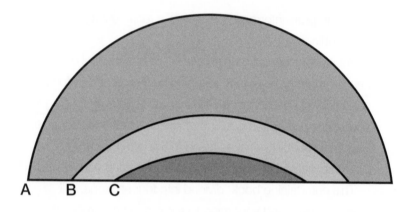

Solution on page 275

Arrowhead Illusion

Can you work out which arrow, A, B, C or D, lines up with the arrowhead? It is not as easy as it seems!

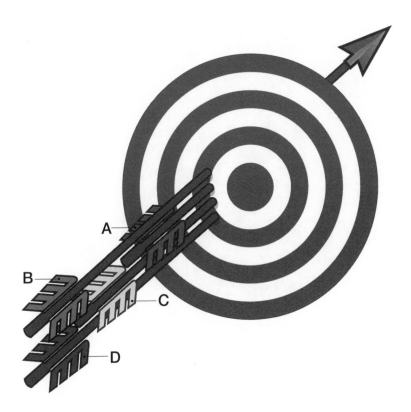

Solution on page 275

Halfway Heart

Does the dot appear less than halfway up the height of the line within the heart?

Solution on page 275

Shepard Tabletop

Are the two tabletops identical in size and shape?

Solution on page 275

Straight — or not?
Is anything in the picture straight?

Solution on page 275

Divergent Crosses

Do the pairs of columns made up of black and white crosses diverge toward the top?

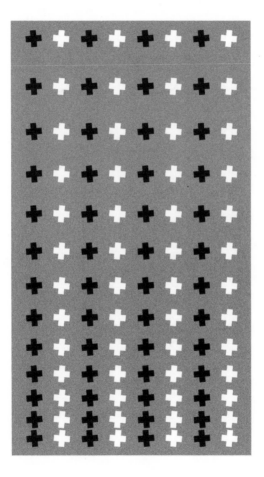

Solution on page 275

Wider or Taller

Is the polo shirt wider (AB) than it is long, or longer (CD) than it is wide? Or are the width and length the same?

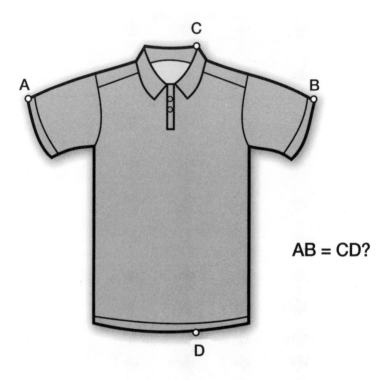

AB = CD?

Solution on page 275

Bowling Ball Size
Are both bowling balls in this picture the same size?

Solution on page 275

Müller-Lyer Illusion

In which figure is the line divided into two equal segments: figure A or figure B?

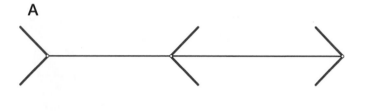

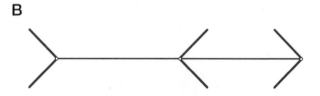

Solution on page 275

Helicopter Lines

Which of the two lines that appear on top of the choppers is longer — the one on the lower helicopter or on the upper one?

Solution on page 275

Rectangle Puzzle

Is the top rectangle (A) the same as the second one (B) in shape and size?

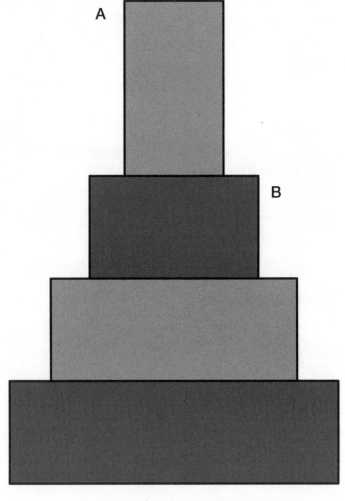

Solution on page 276

Convergent Alignments

Do the two alignments of black and white segments converge toward the top?

Solution on page 276

Delboeuf Illusion

Look at the solid gray discs A, B and C. Which disc is the largest and which is the smallest?

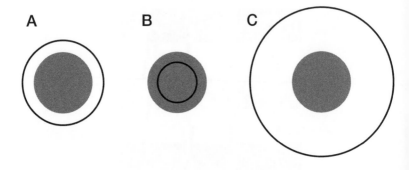

Solution on page 276

Compare the Elephants
Which of these elephants is heavier?

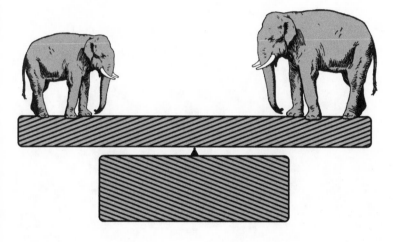

Solution on page 276

The Ames Room

Is the boy a giant?

Solution on page 276

Distorted Squares
Which of these is a true square, A or B?

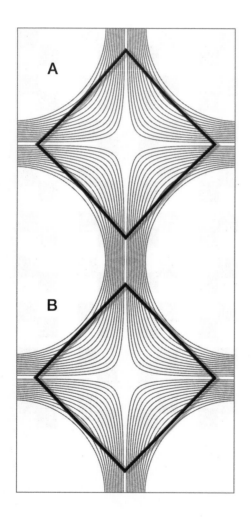

Solution on page 276

Distorted Frame

Are the vertical patterned bands parallel to each other?

Solution on page 276

Spiralling Discs

Observe the disc steadily. How many spirals do you perceive?

Solution on page 276

Pills Series

Are the horizontal lines made with alternating black and white pills straight and parallel to each other?

Solution on page 276

Five Cylinders

The five cylinders seem to meet at a single vanishing point in space. Can you find in the drawing any segments that are perfectly collinear (lying in the same straight line)?

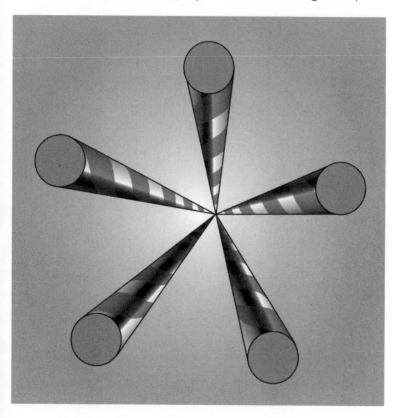

Solution on page 276

Collinear Circles

Which arc, A or B, is perfectly collinear with the circular contour of the wine barrel?

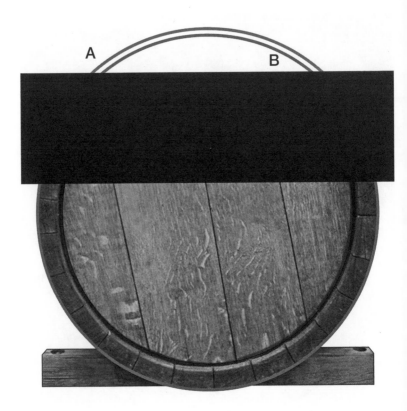

Solution on page 277

Arrows and Circles

Can you decide whether the vertical arrow is longer or shorter than the horizontal one?

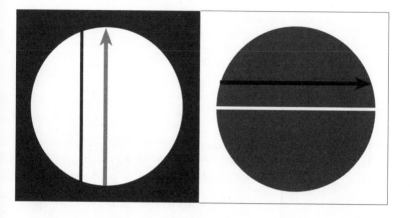

Solution on page 277

Magic Wardrobe
Which vertical black line seems longer: line AB or line CD?

Solution on page 277

Distorted Squares

Are the four wire frames squares? Are they all equal to each other?

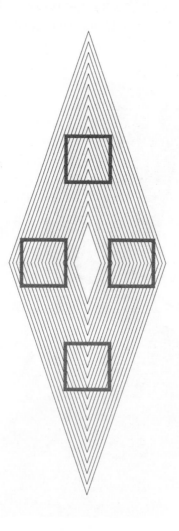

Solution on page 277

Top Hat

In this Belle Époque picture after a drawing by the French artist Edgar Degas you can see a proud gentleman wearing a top hat. Is this top hat wider (AB) than it is tall, or taller (CD) than it is wide?

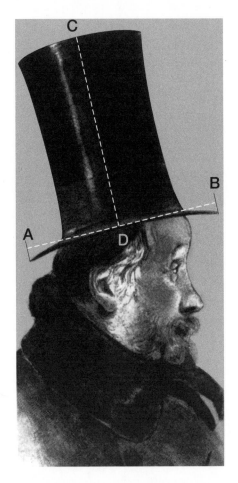

Solution on page 277

Diverging Lines

Are the diagonal lines parallel to each other? Is the background yellowish?

Solution on page 277

Chinese Men

Which of the three Chinese men is the tallest in this vintage picture?

Solution on page 277

Orthogonal tubes

Which angle of the tubular cross is exactly 90 degrees?
Help Jean Vidocq, the Sun King's architect, to find it!

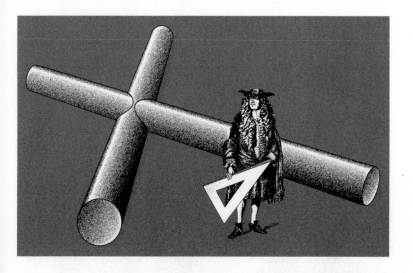

Solution on page 277

Two Chambermaids
At the Palace Hotel, two cleaners have to vacuum the carpets in the corridors on the first floor. In your opinion, which has less work to do — the one with carpet A or the one with carpet B?

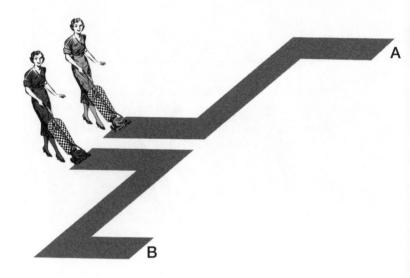

A

B

Solution on page 277

Distorted Legs
Are the legs of these gentlemen bowed or straight?

Solution on page 277

Gerbino's Illusion

Do the black line segments, if connected, appear to form a perfect hexagon?

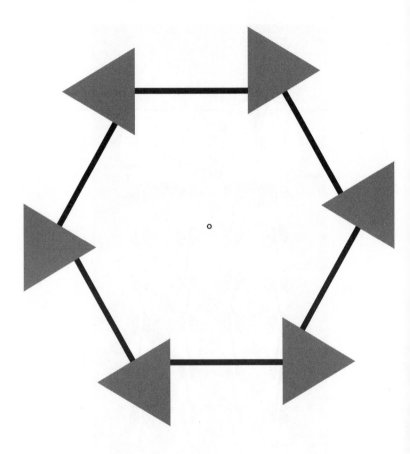

Solution on page 278

Twin Twist
Are these twin sisters the same size?

Solution on page 278

Squares Quandary

Do these quadrilateral shapes have the same surface area?

Solution on page 278

Arches

Are the ribs well formed? Do the curved lines of the arches behind the pillar meet correctly?

Solution on page 278

Dice Dilemma

Are the central gray round dots (pips) of the two dice the same size?

Solution on page 278

Fraser Spiral

Try to follow the spiral in this pattern by tracing just above it with the tip of your finger. You'll find you cannot — but why not?

Solution on page 278

Chinese T

The rods form the Chinese character 'shàng', meaning 'high'. The question is: are the horizontal white and black rods of the same length?

上

Shàng: high

Solution on page 278

Eiffel Tower
Is the man a giant or the Eiffel Tower a scale model?

Solution on page 278

Goldfish
Which goldfish is larger?

Solution on page 278

Coaxial Rings
Do these concentric patterned circles appear to be intertwining or crossing over each other?

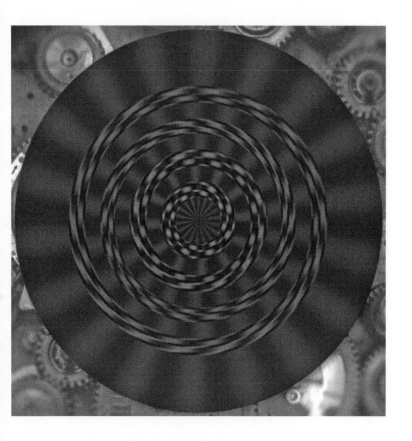

Solution on page 279

Brush Illusion

Which one of the two brushes in Figs A and B has painted the longest stroke?

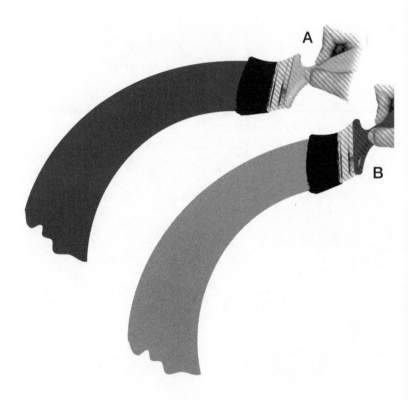

Solution on page 279

Divergent Bands

Are the black columns narrower at the top and the white ones narrower at the bottom?

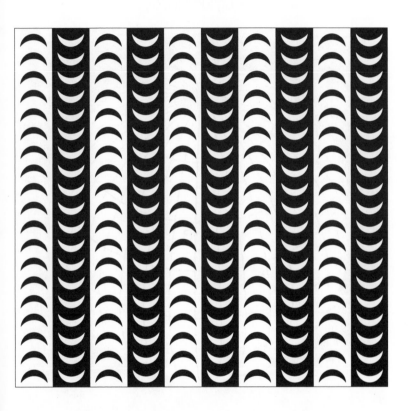

Solution on page 279

Planisphere Center

Which dot is on the midpoint of this planisphere: the dot on the line of latitude (A) or the one on the line of longitude (B)?

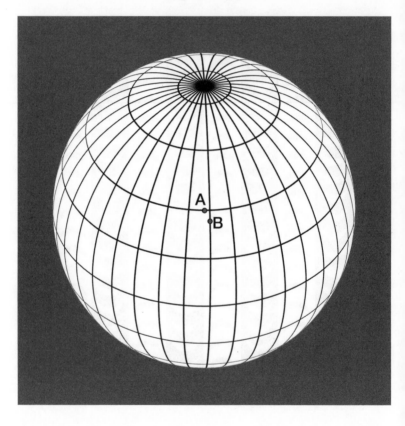

Solution on page 279

Disrupted Lines

Are some of the oblique lines in the picture continuous from one edge to the other?

Solution on page 279

Distorted Wallpaper

Do you feel queasy when you look at this wallpaper? Is there something straight in the wallpaper or is everything askew?

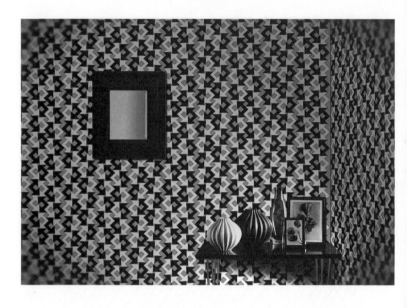

Solution on page 279

Tilting Effect

Are the vertical and horizontal sets of gray lines straight and perpendicular to each other?

Solution on page 279

Bed Length

Which one of these beds — A, B or C — is as long as it is wide?

Solution on page 279

Connected Lines

Two lines, AB and CD, go through the frame. Are the segments of line AB perfectly straight and collinear to each other? And what about line CD?

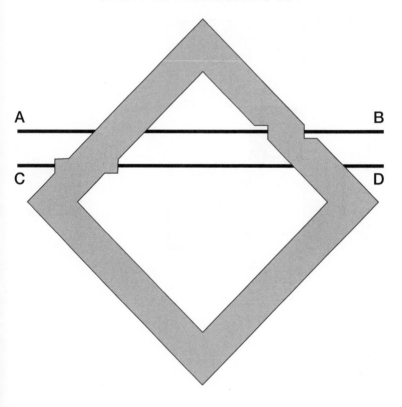

Solution on page 279

Inner Squares
Which inner square is larger: square A or B?

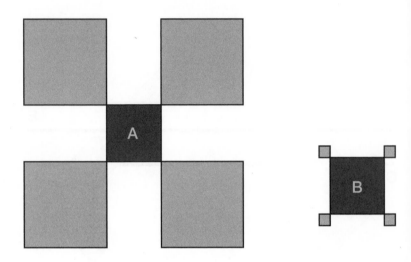

Solution on page 279

Perfect Circle
Is the circle perfectly round?

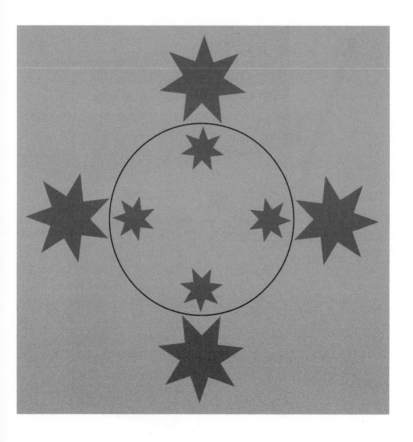

Solution on page 280

Wobbly Walls?

Are the walls skewed? Are the surfaces of the walls different?

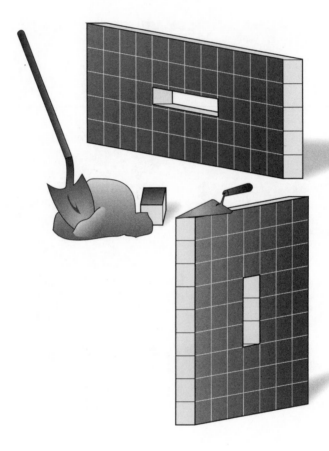

Solution on page 280

Aligned Balls

Are the dark dots collinear (aligned on the same straight line) and parallel to each other?

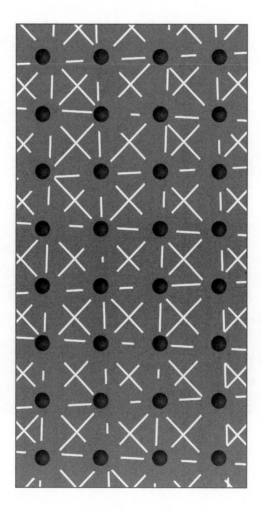

Solution on page 280

Ball Distance

Can you explain why the bright ball seems very slightly larger than the one on the left?

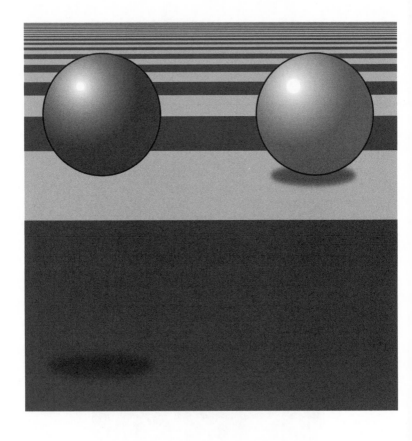

Solution on page 280

Fit the Shapes

Do the shapes fit into each other like Russian dolls?

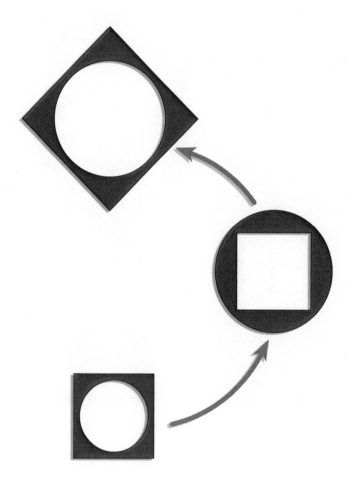

Solution on page 280

Parallel Lines
Are the black lines straight and parallel to each other?

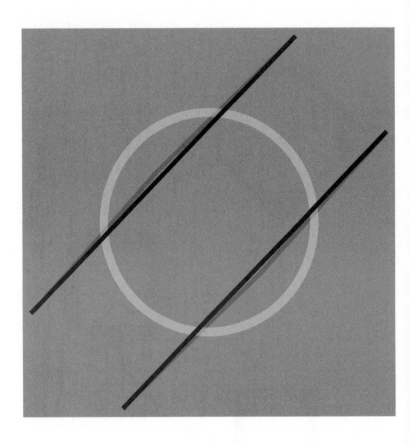

Solution on page 280

Parallel Lines 2
Are the black lines bulging outwards?

Solution on page 280

Middle Point

Which dot is halfway up the distances between the two black bars — dot A, B or C?

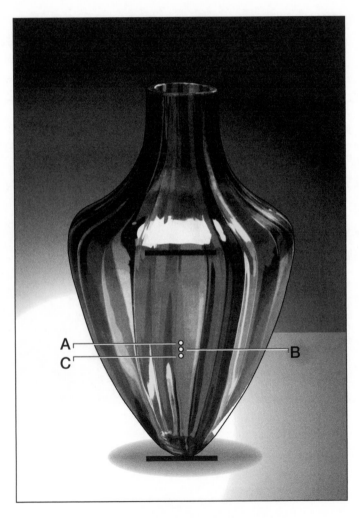

Solution on page 280

Shifting Alignment

If you make the alignment of three dark balls turn around the light ball A (as shown in the image) do you think it will pass through balls A and B without shifting ball B?

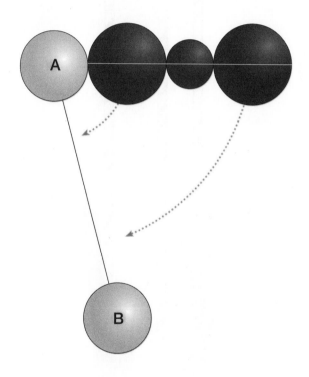

Solution on page 280

Straw Alignment

Is it possible to link the black diagonals on the first, second and third straw together by a continuous diagonal line?

Solution on page 280

Misaligned Edges

Which one of these three shelves has an edge that could be a continuation of one of the edges of the single shelf?

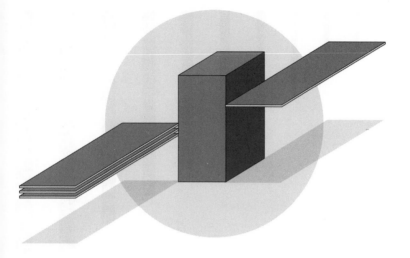

Solution on page 280

Interspace Poles

Are the interspaces between the poles evenly matched?

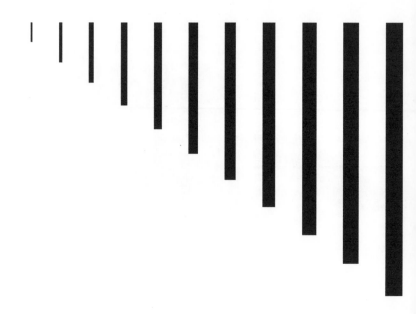

Solution on page 281

Pisa Tower
Which of these paintings hangs slightly askew?

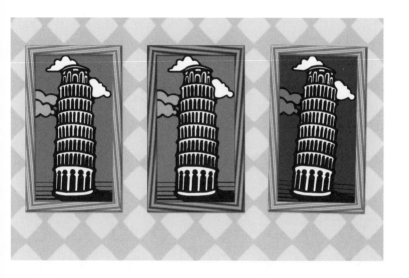

Solution on page 281

Concentric Squares
Are the circular bands of alternate white and black squares perfectly concentric to each other?

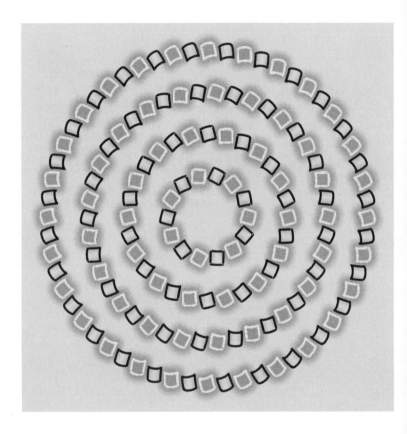

Solution on page 281

Distorted Chequerboard
Are the marquetry elements within the chequerboard center slanted?

Solution on page 281

Aligned SZ Squares

As you can see, alternating black and white capital letters have been distributed on a chequered surface. Are the dark and clear squares distorted?

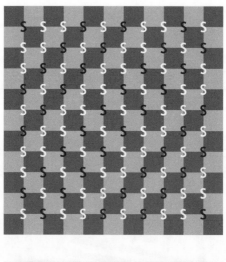

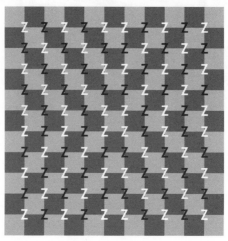

Solution on page 281

Snake Charmer

As if charmed by music, magic ropes spring out from baskets and rise into the air, writhing like snakes. But are the ropes in the picture really contorted?

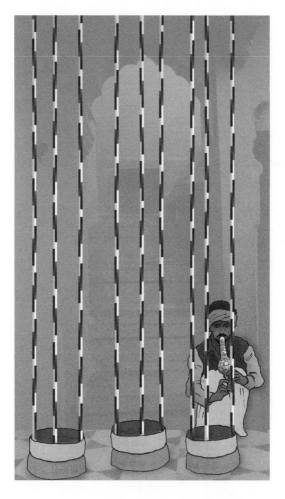

Solution on page 281

Women Divers
Are both divers the same size?

Solution on page 281

Tire Size
Take a careful look at the white lines across the two ellipses which represent the hubcaps of the tractor. Which line is the longest: line A or B?

Solution on page 281

Distorted Squares

Are the four-sided shapes perfect squares?

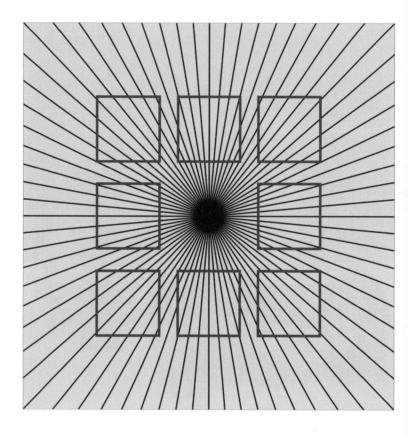

Solution on page 281

Müller-Lyer Variant
Which line is longer, A to B or C to D?

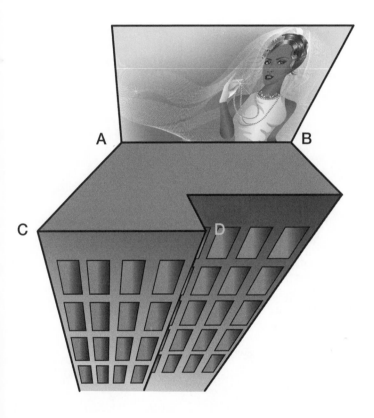

Solution on page 281

Crayon Distortion
Is the ring formed with sliced parts of pencils a perfect circle?

Solution on page 281

AMBIGUOUS AND IMPOSSIBLE FIGURES

Strange Dogs
How many bizarre dogs can you count?

Solution on page 282

Impossible Bars

Which way are the planks facing? If you see errors in the orientation of the items can you redraw them correctly?

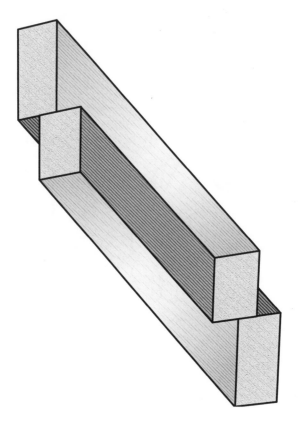

Solution on page 282

Lego Structure
Is it possible to build this structure with Lego blocks?

Solution on page 282

Mystery Woman

Is this woman looking towards you or away from you?

Solution on page 282

How Many Prongs?

How many prongs can you count? Hint: look at the whole length of the middle prong.

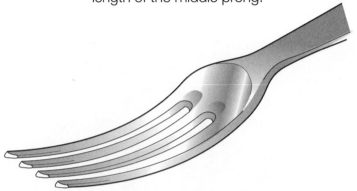

Solution on page 282

Barking Dog

What is the dog barking at?

Solution on page 282

Cat Shadow

Can you tell which is the cat and which is its shadow in this picture?

Solution on page 282

Reversible Head

Try to find the real profession of this pensive man.

Solution on page 283

Silverplate Face
Where is the painter of this still-life painting?

Solution on page 283

Staircase to Nowhere
What happens if the girl climbs the stairs up to the platform?

Solution on page 283

Face Illusion
This picture seems to show trees blowing in the breeze and a boat sailing out to sea at night, yet a woman is hidden in this moonlit landscape! Can you find her?

Solution on page 283

Elephants' Ball
How many legs do these rolling elephants have?

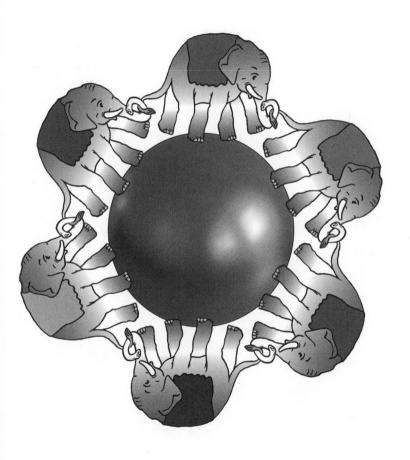

Solution on page 283

Cubic Structure

Do you see this cubic structure from above or from below? Do you notice anything strange?

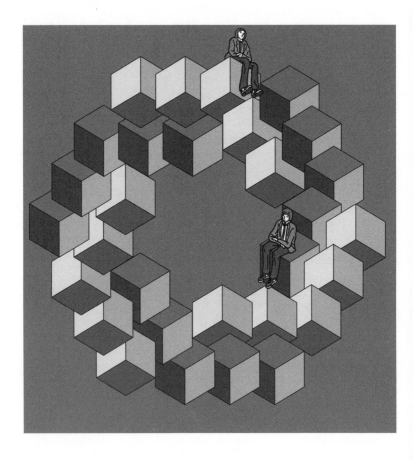

Solution on page 283

Impossible Box

Can you help the boy arrange the construction blocks
into the cardboard box?

Solution on page 283

Piranesi Puzzle

Something in this Gothic picture by the 18th-century Italian artist Piranesi is wrong. Can you tell what?

Solution on page 283

Hearn Illusionist

How many people are in this vintage advertisement for an illusionist?

Solution on page 283

Bear Seal
Do you see a polar bear or a seal?

Solution on page 283

Three Structures

Which one of these enigmatic structures is impossible to build?

Solution on page 283

Double Face

How many women can you see?

Solution on page 284

Ambivalent Terrace

Study both the positioning of the man and the angle of the terrace. Which direction is the man facing?

Solution on page 284

Screws and Washers
Do all the screws fit their respective washers?

Solution on page 284

Impossible Devices

Look at these strange items carefully. Could any of them actually exist in real life, or are they all impossible objects?

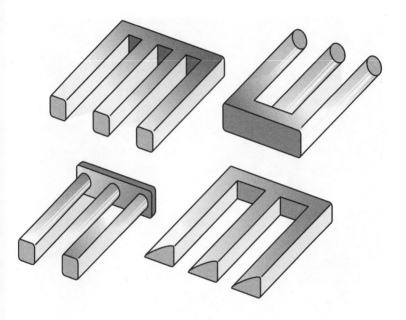

Solution on page 284

Cubic Structure
Why is this cubic structure impossible to build?

Solution on page 284

Labyrinth

Is the snail really imprisoned in this transparent labyrinthine structure?

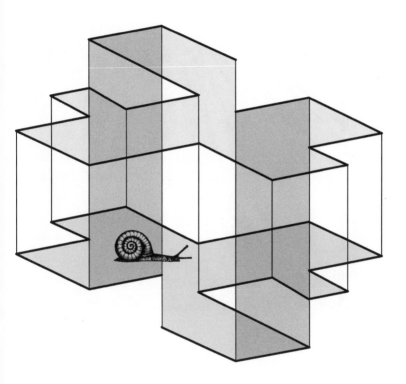

Solution on page 284

Impossible Trees

How many trees can be cut down in this mysterious forest?

Solution on page 284

Impossible Stairs
What is wrong with this picture?

Solution on page 284

Interlaced Rings
Can the rings really be interlaced as shown in the picture?

Solution on page 284

Stairs to Heaven
Why is this an imaginary staircase?

Solution on page 284

Seal Toucan

Can you transform this marine mammal into a bird?

Solution on page 285

Ambivalent Chair

Are you looking at this chair from behind or from the front? Can you be sure?

Solution on page 285

Impossible Wrapping
How would you wrap this crate? Any suggestions?

Solution on page 285

Hidden Birds
How many birds can you find in the picture?

Solution on page 285

Paradoxical Lego Structure
Could you build this structure with Lego blocks?

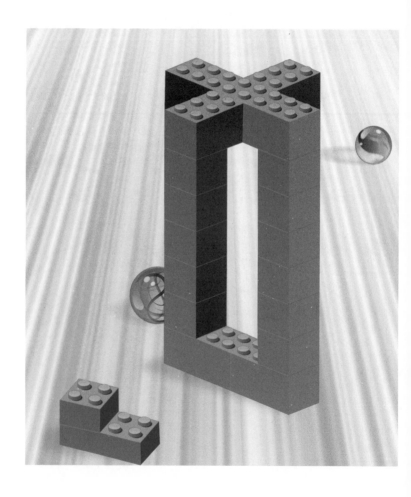

Solution on page 285

Emerging Face

Find a mysterious person in this photograph of the Eiffel Tower.

Solution on page 285

Impossible Band

What is wrong with this structure?

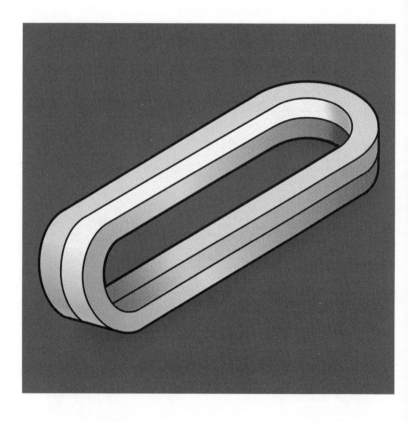

Solution on page 285

Origami Magic
Can you fold a piece of paper as performed by the conjuror?

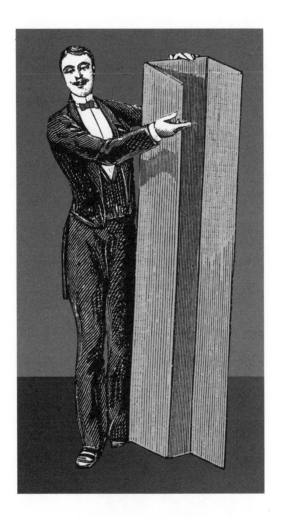

Solution on page 285

Perplexing Architecture
Is this palace possible?

Solution on page 285

Ambiguous Cubes

How many cubes are there in the picture? You may find that the orientation and nature of the shapes change depending on the perspective you adopt.

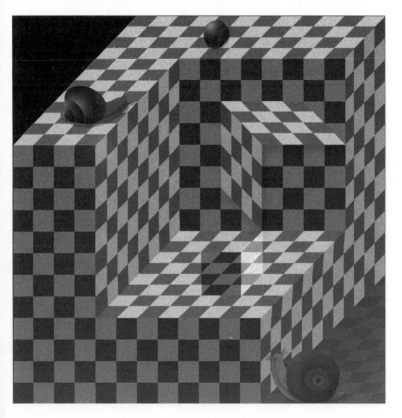

Solution on page 285

Arcade People

Two travelers sit under the arcade while awaiting their tram. But wait . . . what's odd about this picture?

Solution on page 286

Peacock

As conceited as a peacock! Find the vain man in the bird.

Solution on page 286

Three Women
You can see two women, but where is the third?

Solution on page 286

Something Looms

Find what is hidden within this picture, representing Pierrot declaring his love to Columbine.

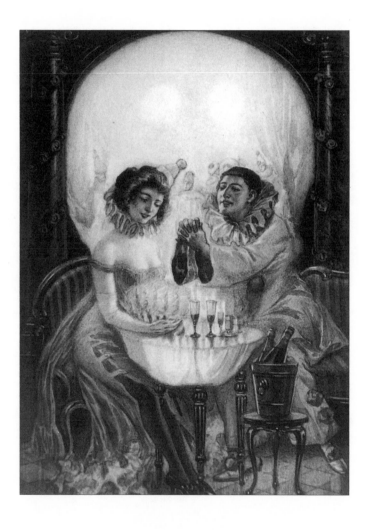

Solution on page 286

Earth Woman
Do you see something strange in this globe?

Solution on page 286

Penrose Stairs Variant

If the two men in the picture walk continuously on this staircase construction, what will happen?

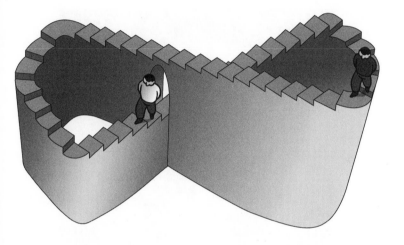

Solution on page 286

Mirror Devil
What are the two women talking about?

Solution on page 286

Camouflage Stripes
What can you see here?

Solution on page 286

Perpetual Motion
Will the ball roll down forever on the inclined planks of this perpetual motion device?

Solution on page 286

Vasarely Structure

How would you describe the strange volume shown in the picture?

Solution on page 286

Magnetic Eyes

Does the woman on this book cover illustration by Aleksandr Rodchenko (1923) look directly at you, even if you move to the right or left?

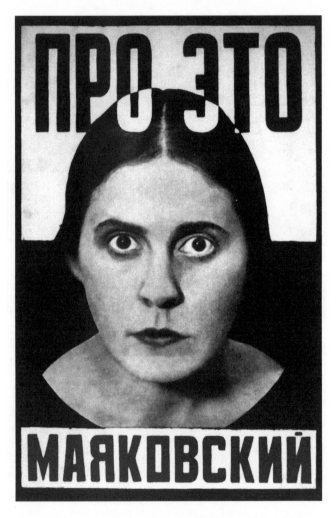

Solution on page 286

Ambiguous Car

Could you drive such an ancient car? What is wrong with it?

Solution on page 286

Sea Legs

At first glance this might seem like a normal line of sailors, but look carefully. Can you see something strange going on with their legs?

Solution on page 287

Strange Cylinders

Take a piece of paper and try to fold it in order to reproduce any of the spiraling structures shown in the picture. Is this possible?

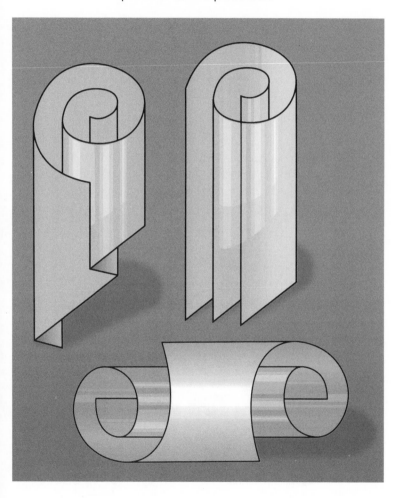

Solution on page 287

Impossible Vault
Would your money be safe in this vault?

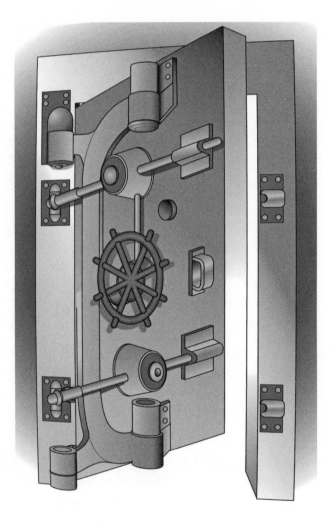

Solution on page 287

Acrobat Girl
What is wrong with this picture?

Solution on page 287

Impossible Die

'The die is cast!' said Caesar. But no one could throw the die depicted here. Why not?

Solution on page 287

Tennis

Maybe there is something wrong with this tennis court?

Solution on page 287

Mystery House

Find three strange perspective errors in the picture.

Solution on page 287

Impossible Bicycle
Will the front wheel of this toy bicycle turn freely?

Solution on page 287

Odd Pentagon
What is wrong with this Z-shaped board?

Solution on page 287

Missing Bottle

There was a party, but where is the bottle? Do you see another oddity?

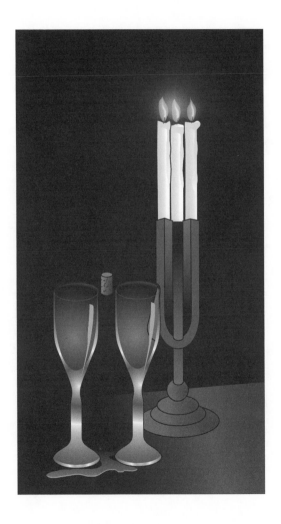

Solution on page 287

A Question of Columns

There are five oddities in the picture. Can you find them all?

Solution on page 287

Confusing Colanders
Can you say which colander is showing its convex side,
and which its concave side?

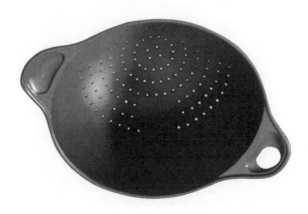

Solution on page 287

Up or Down
Is the man at the center of the picture ascending or descending the stairs? Could you get to the top of these stairs?

Solution on page 288

Globes

Two globes, or just one hollow sphere with a large circular hole?

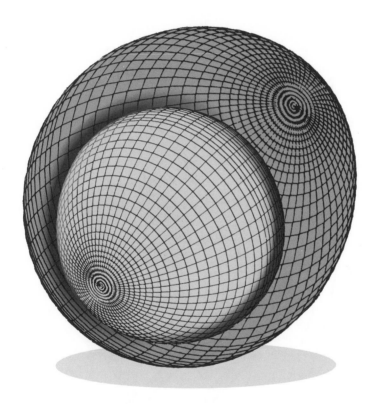

Solution on page 288

Reader

Are you really behind this seated man reading a newspaper?

Solution on page 288

Cubic Structure

Does this curious cubic structure have a top and a bottom
or is it flat?

Solution on page 288

Henry VIII and Anne of Cleves

This is a caricature of King Henry VIII. Can you find his fourth wife, Anne of Cleves?

Solution on page 288

Mountain Magic
Look carefully at this Chinese landscape and you may uncover a mystery.

Solution on page 288

Ratting Cat
This black cat is on the hunt for mice and rats:
can you find its prey?

Solution on page 288

Masked Lovers

The picture shows a mask of a pensive person. But is it a woman or a man?

Solution on page 288

Old Young Man
Where is the father of this young man?

Solution on page 288

Reverse Side Painting
Is this actually the back or the front of a painting?

Solution on page 288

BRIGHTNESS AND MOVEMENT ILLUSIONS

Scintillating Discs
Do you notice something unusual about these sun-like shapes?

Solution on page 289

Christmas Lights

Why do these lights appear to be winking and flickering?

Solution on page 289

Map Illusion

Is the land in this map of Europe and North Africa shaded with clear gray?

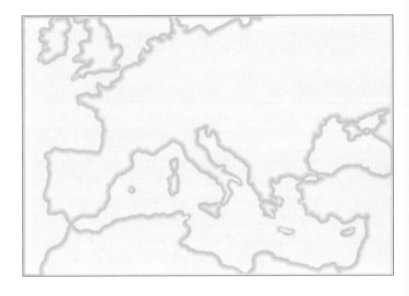

Solution on page 289

Chaotic Texture

Move your eyes around this image. Do you notice anything in particular?

Solution on page 289

Camouflaged Balls

How many balls can you distinguish from the background?

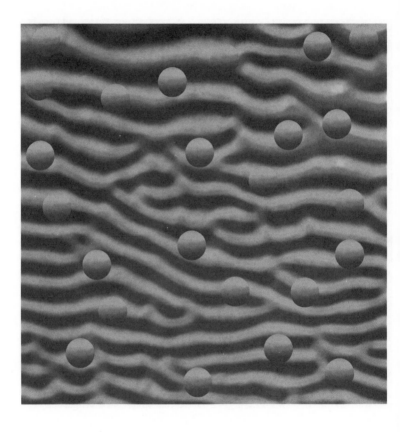

Solution on page 289

Spinning Vortex
Why are the small white dots twinkling slightly?

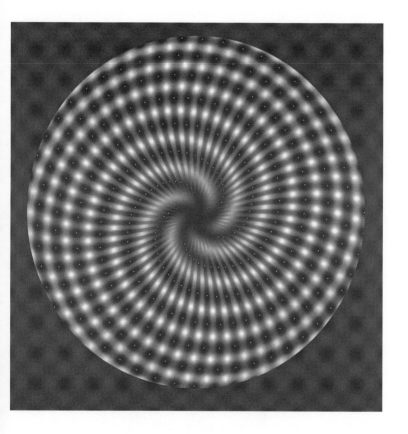

Solution on page 289

Square Composition

Look at the two checkered arrangements A and B.
Are they the same?

A

B

Solution on page 289

Vibrating Discs

When you look at these, do the concentric rings appear to rotate? Does the center of the patterns whirl and scintillate?

Solution on page 289

Gray-shaded Squares
Are all the gray squares the same shade?

Solution on page 290

Rotation Arcs

Are the four rings concentric, sharing exactly the same center? What happens if you move your head back and forth while you stare at the central cross?

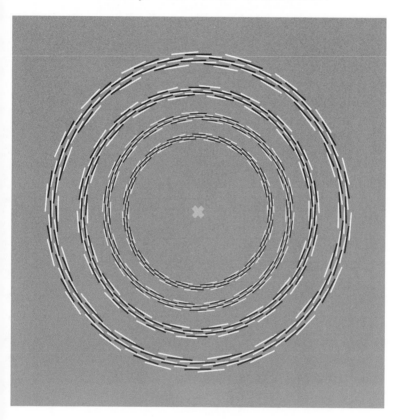

Solution on page 290

Gray Cross
Can you say which of the spots are darker and lighter?

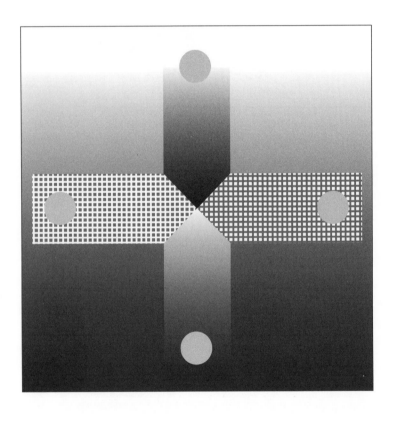

Solution on page 290

Stubbs Illusion

Fix your gaze steadily on the center of the image and see what happens. Now move your eyes away from the center of the pattern — do you notice something strange?

Solution on page 290

Moving Smudges

Move your eyes around these groups of smudged marks. What do you experience?

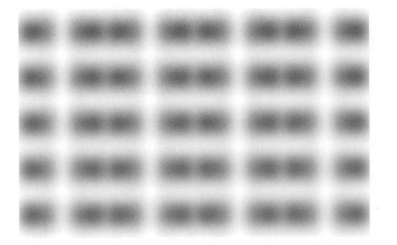

Solution on page 290

Madonna Afterimage

Stare at the middle of the black picture for about 30 seconds, then immediately close your eyes and tilt your head back. Keep your eyes closed for a little while. What do you 'see'?

Solution on page 290

Disappearing Eye
Concentrate on the middle of the black schematic eye for at least 20 seconds. What happens?

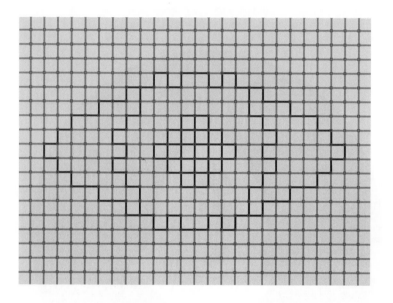

Solution on page 290

Moving Rays
What happens to the image if you move the page slightly?

Solution on page 290

Misleading Stripes

Is the rectangle A wider and brighter than the gray rectangle B?

Solution on page 290

Celtic Patterns

Are the curvilinear patterns in the rectangles A, B, C and D of the same shade?

A

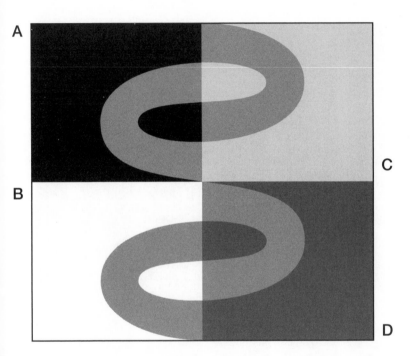

B

C

D

Solution on page 290

Neon Brightness

Four gray stripes seem to float over the neon tubes shown here. Are these stripes uniformly gray?

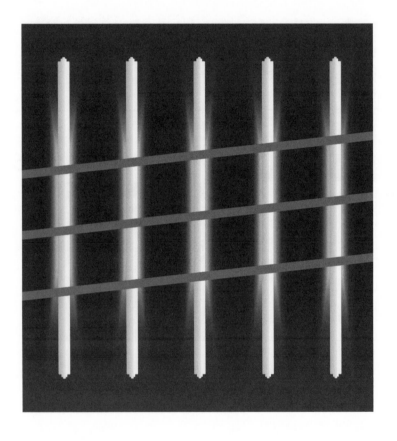

Solution on page 290

White Effect
Which set of gray bars is clearer and which one is darker?

Solution on page 290

Ehrenstein Figure

Do you perceive circles that appear brighter than their surroundings?

Solution on page 290

Rotating Spirals
How many spirals can you see? Do you experience
something unusual while looking at the picture?

Solution on page 291

Cat Sofa

Which stripe on the sofa, B or C, has exactly the same gray tone as stripe A?

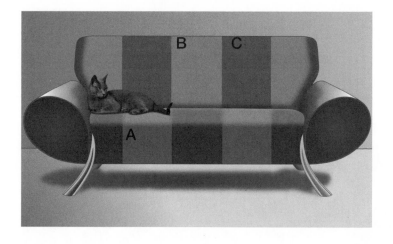

Solution on page 291

Concentric Swarming
What happens if you concentrate on the circular rings?

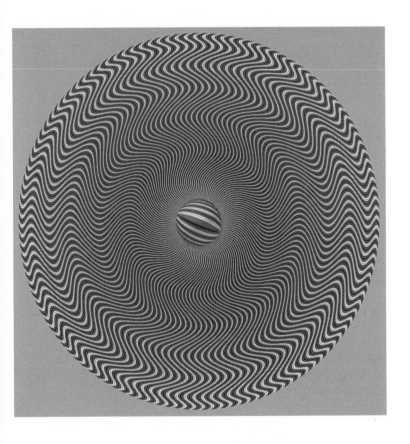

Solution on page 291

Nureyev Illusion
Does the dancer float in the air?

Solution on page 291

Hermann Grid
Can you see the ghostly gray spots at the intersections?
Stare at one of them — what happens?

Solution on page 291

Squares of Confusion

Look at this picture for a while — what do you notice?
How many different types of gray shapes are there in
the picture?

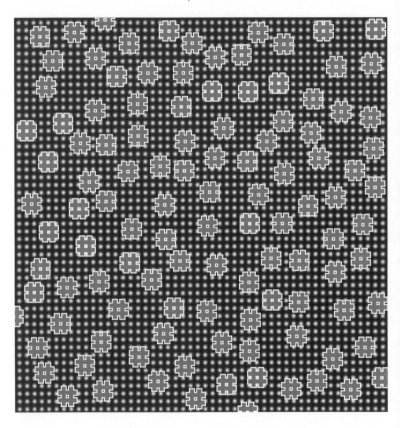

Solution on page 291

Tonal Illusion

Which ball corresponds exactly to ball A — ball B or ball C?

Solution on page 291

Levitating Ball

Does the ball move slightly and levitate? (Moving the image horizontally or vertically will give a much stronger effect.)

Solution on page 291

Explosion

While you are staring at the central ball, do you get the impression that it is floating and moving slightly? Now, move the page towards you and away from you. Do you notice something special?

Solution on page 291

Pulsating Pattern

Stare at the image and note all the visual illusions you can see.

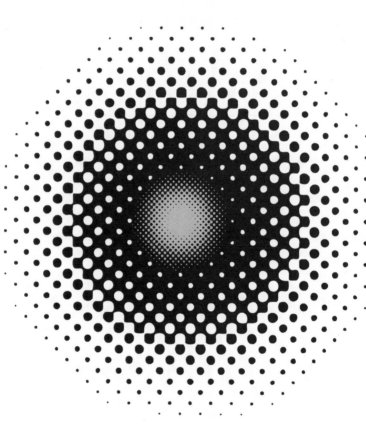

Solution on page 291

Moving Arcs
What happens if you blink while looking at this pattern?

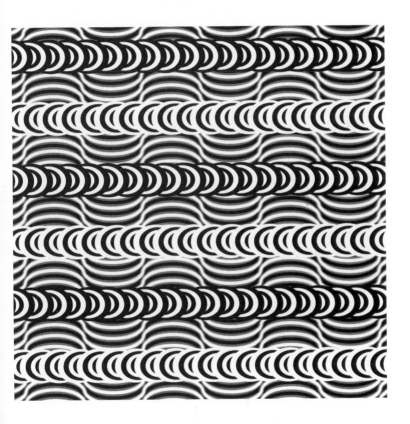

Solution on page 292

Fairies

Observe the seated fairy in both photographs. The second photograph is the negative of the first one. Are her wings of the same hue?

Solution on page 292

Moving Lines

Sweep your eyes around the pattern to see what the thin vertical lines will do.

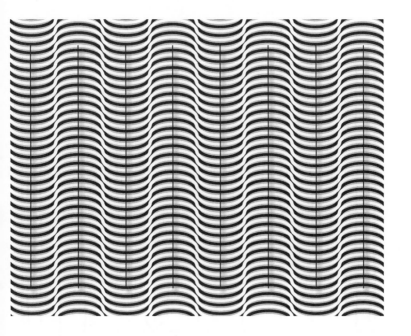

Solution on page 292

Illusory Squares and Discs

Can you see squares and bright discs here? Why might this be?

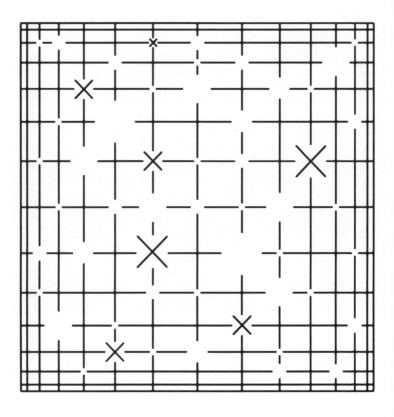

Solution on page 292

Brightness and Contrast Bars

Which gray bar — A or B — corresponds to the bar lying on the contrasted background?

A

B

Solution on page 292

Grid Illusion

Shift your gaze around the grid design. Do you notice something strange?

Solution on page 292

Rotating Patterns

Move your head back and forth, keeping the focus on the central cross of the image. What do you perceive?

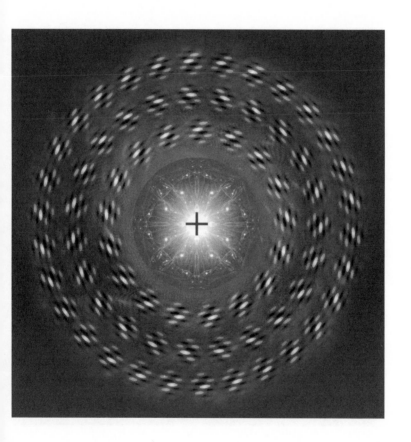

Solution on page 292

Spots or Not?
Are there two distinct sets of gray spots here?

Solution on page 292

Follow My Eyes

1. Stare at the center of the geometric picture shown. Keeping your gaze fixed on the central spot, move your head backwards and forwards several times. What happens?
2. Keeping the image 12in (30cm) away from your eyes, tilt the page from side to side with a gentle swinging movement. What do you see now?

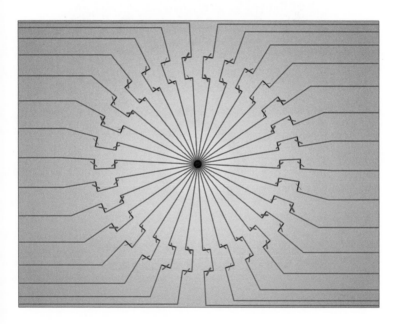

Solution on page 292

Floating Balls

This illusion works best with bright lighting. Look around the picture in a relaxed way — don't focus directly on it but off to the side (x). Do you now perceive something strange?

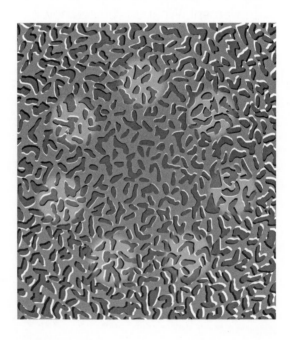

Solution on page 293

Radial Pulses
Stare at the center of this radial pattern.
What appears to happen?

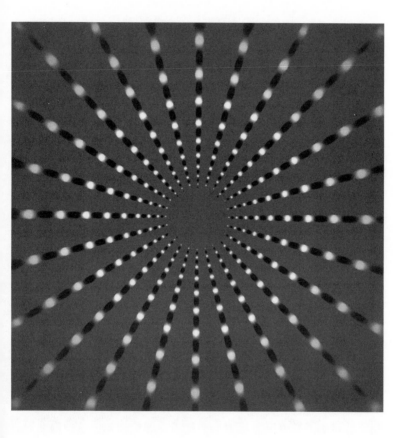

Solution on page 293

Black Patches

Is this series of black patches blurred? What happens when you sweep your gaze around this pattern?

Solution on page 293

Vasarely Adaptation
Do you perceive bright diagonals crossing each of the shaded squares?

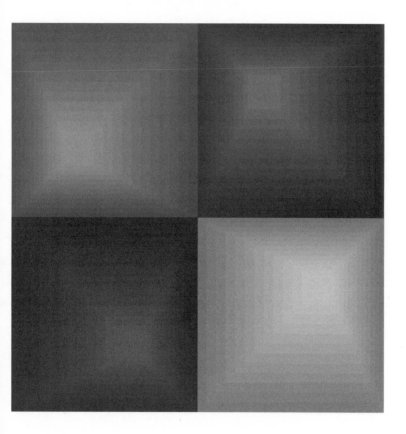

Solution on page 293

Disappearing Face
Close one eye and focus your attention on the nose of the face for about 20–30 seconds.
What do you experience?

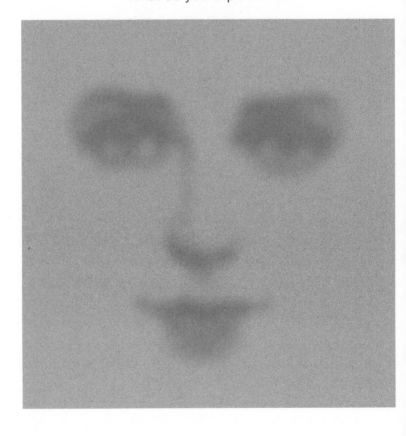

Solution on page 293

VISUAL AND COGNITIVE TESTS

Tool Search
How many tools can you find in the picture?

Solution on page 294

Someone in the Sunset
Someone is hidden in the sunset — can you guess who?

Solution on page 294

Hidden Animal

Which animal has been carved into the wooden board?

Solution on page 294

Black and White Confusion
What does this picture represent?

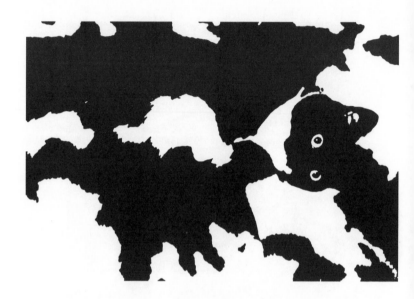

Solution on page 294

Find the Cross

Look for the cross in the square.

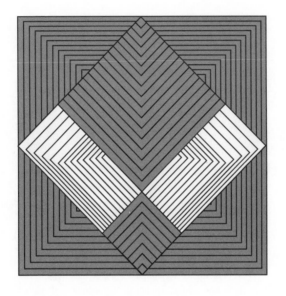

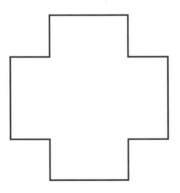

Solution on page 294

Ant Army

Without counting them, are there more black ants or white ants? Is the square formation straight or is it slanted?

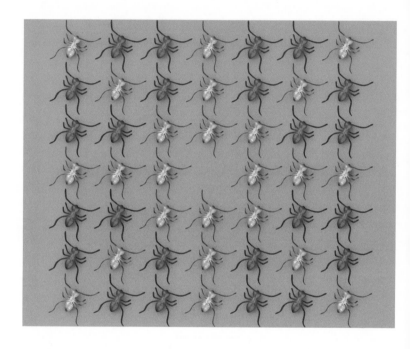

Solution on page 294

William Tell Illusion

How many arrows can you see? Are you sure?
Count them again.

Solution on page 294

Old Swiss Mill

Can you find all the animals and faces hidden in this famous print by Currier and Ives? As a clue, many of the figures form part of other figures.

Solution on page 295

Clock Test

There are exactly five distinct types of clock. Which batch has to be eliminated to get the same number of each kind of clock?

Solution on page 295

Hidden in a Horse
Find the kissing cowgirl's boyfriend!

Solution on page 295

Tricky Calculator
Add in your head the numbers shown on this page by following the instructions. Write down the final result on a piece of paper. Then check the result with a calculator. What do you get?

Take 1000 and add 40 to it.

Now add another 1000.

Now ADD 30.

Add another 1000.

Now add 20.

Now add another 1000.

Finally add 10.

What is the total?

Solution on page 295

Mystery Photo
What does this intriguing vintage photo show? A very ugly man, perhaps?

Solution on page 295

Dartboard Doubt

Is the area of the outer dark ring larger or smaller than the inner clear disc?

Solution on page 295

Broken Dish

Can you repair this dish? Hint: try to concentrate on one of the lobster's eyes . . .

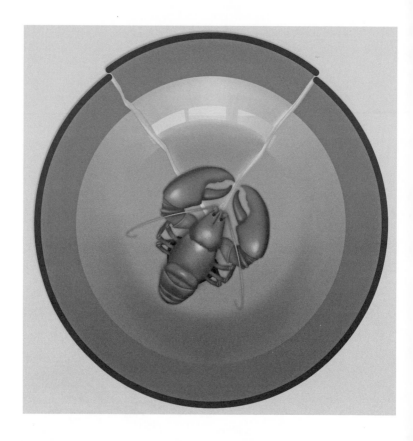

Solution on page 295

Panda Puzzle
Help mother panda to find her cub and her companion!

Solution on page 295

Dots to Squares

It is easy to draw two squares using all eight dots — but can you delimit just one perfect square (the ring) by connecting all the dots?

Solution on page 295

Snap-hooks

A chain of 15 linked snap-hooks is separated into five smaller parts by opening just four single snap-hooks. Could you link the five chain portions to form the initial chain again by opening only three single snap-hooks?

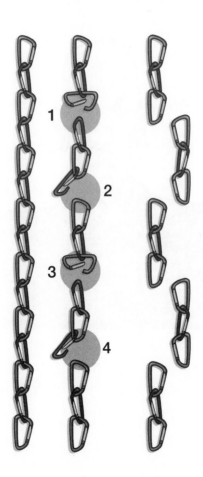

Solution on page 295

Complete the Drawing

The image is missing critical information. Is the man depicted in the picture a cartoon-type hulk, or something else? Try to complete the drawing using your sense of humor and visual imagination.

Solution on page 296

Rorschach Test

Here's a psychological test: what does this inkblot represent for you?

Solution on page 296

Unbroken Line

Try to draw a continuous line without lifting your pen in order to reproduce this pattern.

Solution on page 296

Shape Shading
How many areas are concave? And how many are convex? Turn the picture upside-down and count again. What happens?

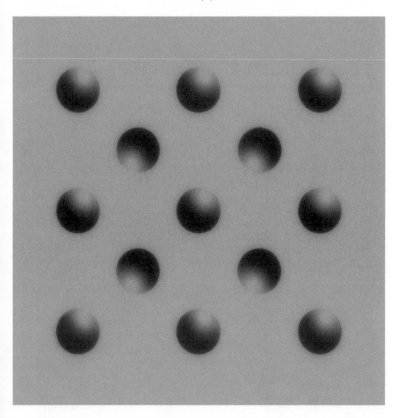

Solution on page 296

Coffee Beans
Try to find the child in the coffee beans pile!

Solution on page 296

Glass Experiment
Is this image real or is it a photomontage?

Solution on page 296

Gears
Why couldn't this strange mechanical gadget work?

Solution on page 296

Psychedelic Puzzle
What does the picture represent?

Solution on page 297

Find the Animal
Which animal is hidden in the picture?

Solution on page 297

Caught in a Loop

In which loop, A or B, may your finger be gripped if the string ends are drawn?

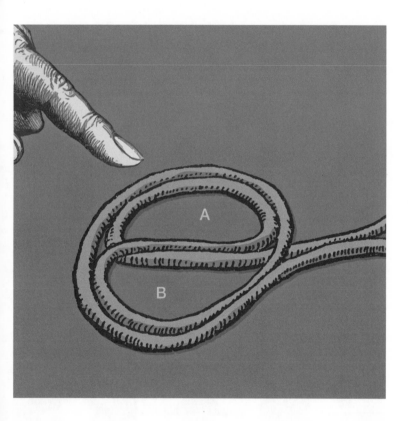

Solution on page 297

Find the Arrows

To test your visual attention, see how many arrows you can find in this pattern.

Solution on page 297

Path Problem 1

To test your visuospatial logic, draw lines within the whole shape to join like symbols together (triangle to triangle, etc.), without any line crossing another line.

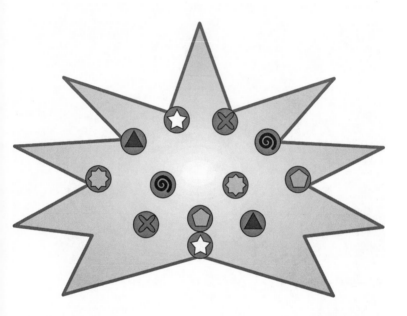

Solution on page 297

Halloween Popcorn
How many spooky skulls can you spot in this bowl
of popcorn?

Solution on page 297

Path Problem 2

Draw lines within the box to join matching symbols together (triangle to triangle and so on), without any line crossing another line.

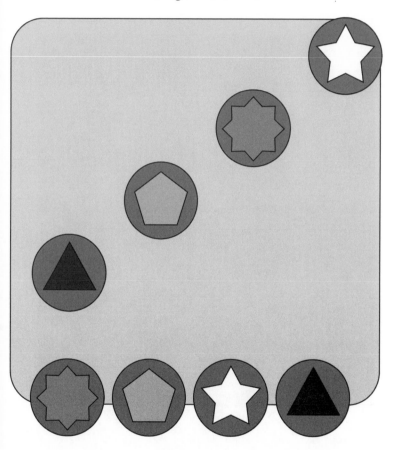

Solution on page 298

Hidden Elephants
Find four elephants in the puzzle pieces!

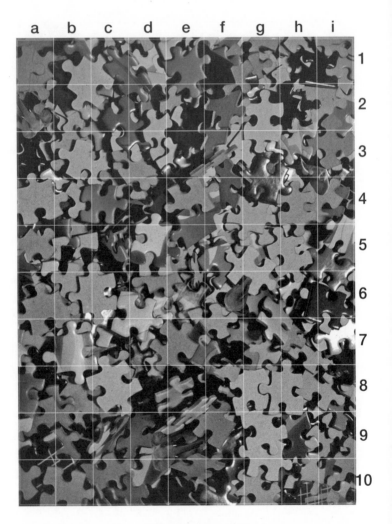

Solution on page 298

Handprint Illusion

In this handprint you can see more than just a hand in it — there is the image of an animal. Can you spot it?

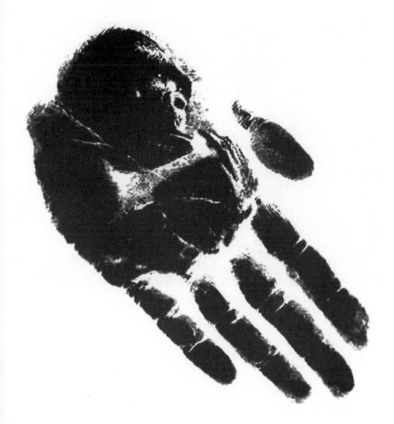

Solution on page 298

Tiger Face

A tourist took this photograph of a tiger when traveling in India and noticed afterwards that there was a child camouflaged in the picture. Where is he?

Solution on page 298

Hidden Girl

Is the rower being watched?

Solution on page 298

Hidden Squares

Try to find as many squares as you can in this geometric diagram.

Solution on page 298

Hidden Zebra

Find the other three zebras within this African savanna.

Solution on page 298

Multiple Babies
How many babies can you count in this picture?

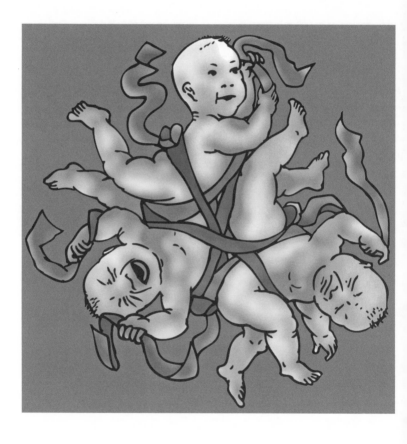

Solution on page 299

Hidden Discs

How many circles do you see in this pattern?

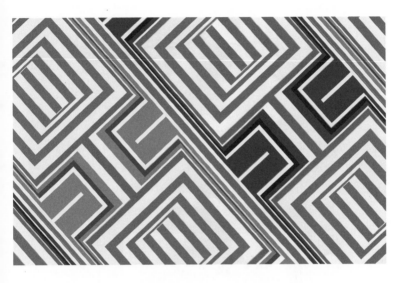

Solution on page 299

Magic Pin

To test your visual thinking, which pin — A or B — should be removed to make the picture fall to the ground?

Solution on page 299

Impossible Paths

To test your visual logic, starting from the small X, draw the shortest path that includes all the fir trees. No line can include any black dot or touch any white dot.

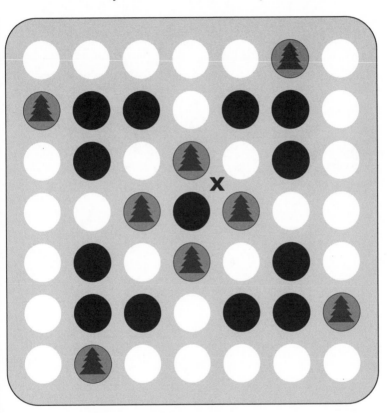

Solution on page 299

Making Contact

Can you magically make the forefingers taken from Michelangelo's fresco in the Sistine Chapel touch each other?

Solution on page 299

Sailor Thoughts

On dry land, sailors typically have just one obsession.
Can you guess what the sailor is looking for?

Solution on page 299

Old and Young

Where is the grandmother of this young girl?

Solution on page 299

Blivet Structure

Is the lintel of this ancient stone ruin supported by two or three legs?

Solution on page 299

Shadow
Is this black and white picture meaningful?

Solution on page 300

The Long View

The telescope shown in the picture is split into two pieces and between them lies a boulder. Explain how the gentleman can still see the rose placed in front of the lens (hint: it is just a question of reflections).

Solution on page 300

Rabbit Hunter

In this vintage picture puzzle, find a man shooting a rabbit.

Solution on page 300

Herd of Elephants

Can you count how many elephants are in this picture, an example of vintage matchbox art?

Solution on page 300

Marbles Test

Spot all the white-and-gray marbles in the picture. Time allowed: 1 minute!

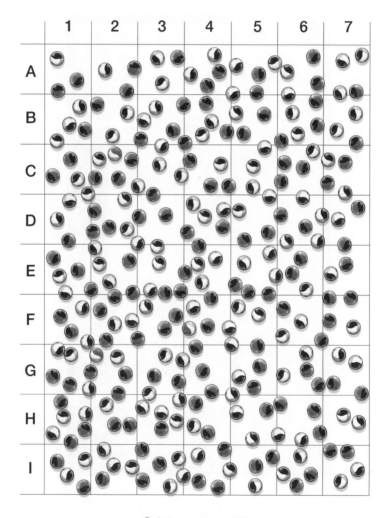

Solution on page 300

Bewildered Hunter

Can you spot the hidden deer, tiger, bear, and men's and women's faces in this picture puzzle by printers Nathaniel Currier and James Merrit Ives, titled *The Bewildered Hunter* (1872)?

Solution on page 300

Fox Puzzle

In *The Puzzled Fox*, also produced by printers Currier and Ives in 1872, there are many more characters than you may at first think. See if you can spot the horse, lamb, wild boar and numerous faces of men and women.

Solution on page 300

Ambiguous Cheese
What does this drawing represent?

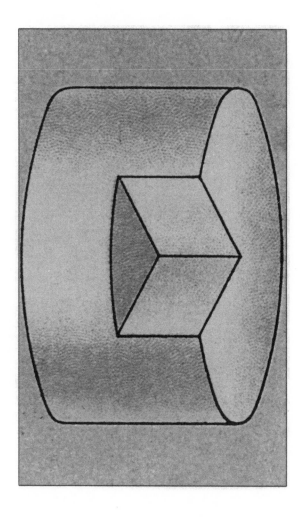

Solution on page 301

Rectangle Square

Which geometric shape is more like the four-sided figure ABCD: the shape shown in Figs a), b) or c)?

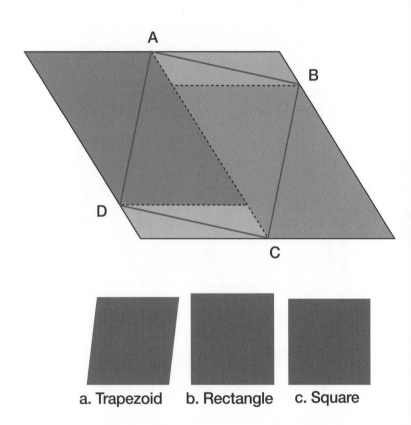

a. Trapezoid   b. Rectangle   c. Square

Solution on page 301

Frankenstein's Dream

Look at Frankenstein from a certain distance — approximately 8ft (2.4m) — and you will see what he is dreaming about.

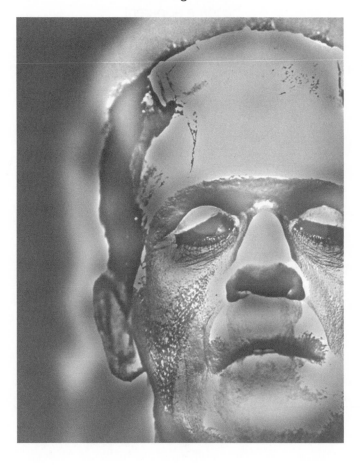

Solution on page 301

Gestalt Test

The whole is different to the sum of the parts: can you guess what the overall image represents? Only a jumble of dark shapes? Look again and it will suddenly become apparent!

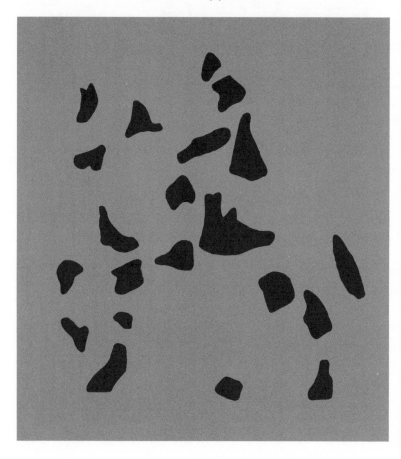

Solution on page 301

Cow Drinking

Here is an amusing illusion. Look at the picture while repeating the word 'white' out loud ten times. Now answer this question quickly: 'What does a cow drink?'

Solution on page 301

Kersten Ball

Are the balls in the two pictures in different positions relative to the background?

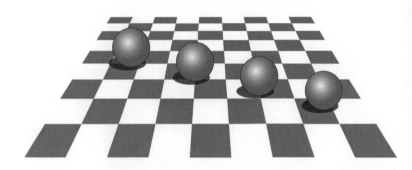

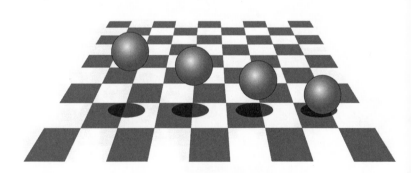

Solution on page 301

Ambiguous Cubes
What happens if you turn the picture upside-down?

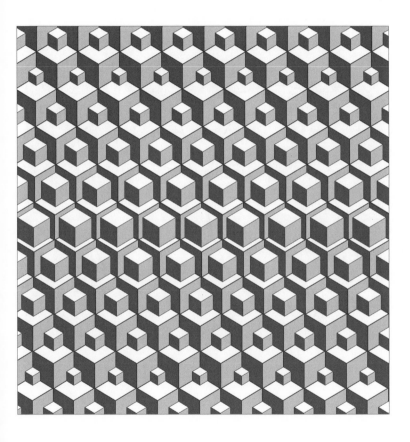

Solution on page 301

Multiple Horses
How many horses can you perceive in the picture?

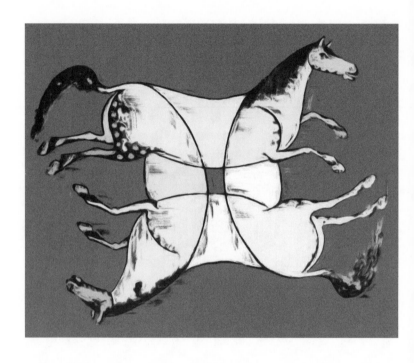

Solution on page 301

Invisible Woman

Do you see a woman in the picture or it is just your imagination?

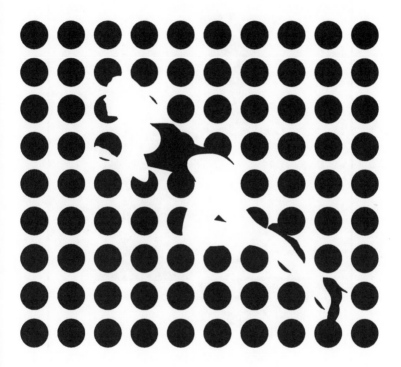

Solution on page 301

Talking Cups
These cups are telling a short story. Can you follow it?

Solution on page 302

Reversed Faces

Find two big differences between the boys (if you can't, turn the picture upside-down).

Solution on page 302

How Many Triangles?
How many triangles can you perceive in the picture?

Solution on page 302

Perceptual Set

Though the picture is mostly dark and incomplete, we can still make out . . . what?

Solution on page 302

Shapes Puzzle

Which shape — a), b) or c) — fits exactly into the pentagonal hole?

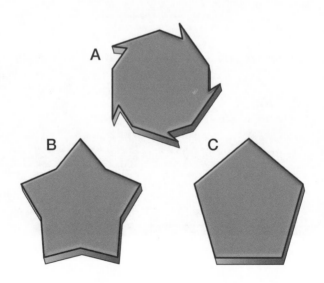

Solution on page 302

Cheese Vision
Which piece of cheese is cut from the semi-circular
Emmenthal cheese?

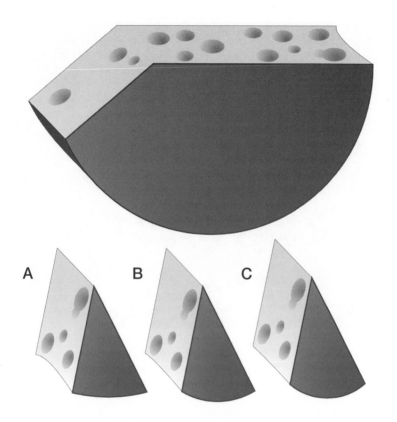

A

B

C

Solution on page 302

Seeing Double
What is the trouble with this strange woman?

Solution on page 302

Follow Your Star

Find the star shown in Fig. A in the pattern.

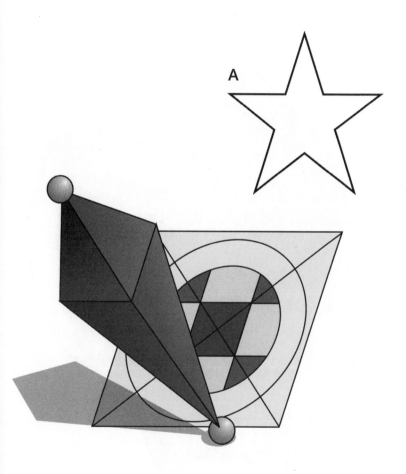

Solution on page 302

Dog or Not?

Is this an ugly boxer dog? What else could it be?

Solution on page 303

Bidirectional Face

Move to your left or to your right while looking at the hypnotic eyes in this face — what happens?

Solution on page 303

Pipes Connection Test

We have laid on water, internet connections and electricity from the utility suppliers W, O and L to each of the three houses A, B and C without any pipe crossing another. Can you check if the work has been done properly?

Solution on page 303

Blind Spot

Hold the picture 12in (30cm) in front of you and close your right eye. Focus on a number at a time, starting with 1, and count up slowly. Do you notice something interesting?

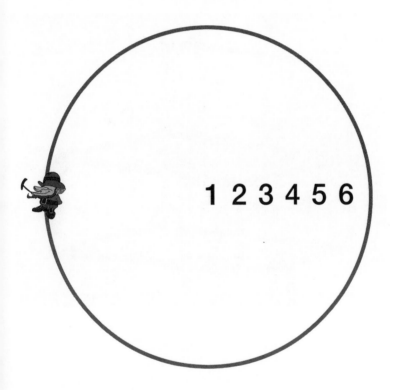

Solution on page 303

Strange Box

Are you looking at this strange box at eye level or from behind and below?

Solution on page 303

Cat-fly Blindspot

Close your right eye and hold this page about 12 in (30 cm) from your left eye. Look at the nose of the cat and slowly move the page forwards and backwards until the fly on its whisker disappears. Why does this happen?

Solution on page 303

Gear Belt Puzzle 1

Only one device allows Fred to run freely without getting stuck: is it device A or B?

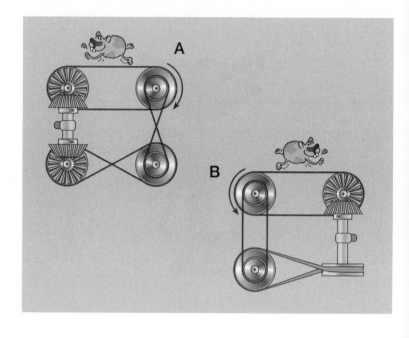

Solution on page 303

Disco Dance
These dancers are having fun, but are they alone?

Solution on page 304

Buddha Among the Leaves
Find the face of Buddha in the leaves. Don't stress —
some people have taken 15 minutes to find it!

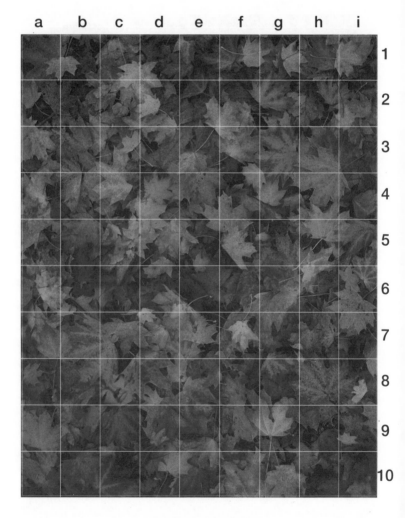

Solution on page 304

Collinear Circles (page 26) See the picture for the answer.

Arrows and Circles (page 27) Though the vertical arrow appears longer, both arrows are of the same length. Despite our ability to correctly estimate size differences in many cases, we can be misled by a wide range of factors and even a simple arrangement of lines.

Magic Wardrobe (page 28) They are equal in length.

Distorted Squares (page 29) The four wire frames are perfect equal squares.

Top Hat (page 30) Even though it seems unbelievable, the brim of the top hat is broader than its height!

Diverging Lines (page 31) Though they appear to be divergent, the diagonal lines are perfectly straight and parallel to each other. The background is uniformly white.

Chinese Men (page 32) Curiously enough, the man in the foreground is 15 per cent taller than the one in the background. This is a neat variant of the Ponzo illusion.

Othogonal Tubes (page 33) See the image. Because of the perspective bias, the 90-degree angle doesn't look very convincing, but checking with a set square will prove it to you.

Two Chambermaids (page 34) Both carpets are the same length (see the picture) so the work is evenly distributed.

Distorted Legs (page 35) Straight! Take a pencil or a ruler and check it. This is a variant of Fraser illusion.

Gerbino's Illusion (page 36) Yes, the black straight-line segments form a perfect hexagon. Any regular shape can be misperceived when its angles are asymmetrically occluded by triangles: our mind projects the line that runs into the midpoint of a triangle to its center, rather than continuing to the point where it should meet the other line. This illusion is known as off-kilter or Gerbino's illusion.

Twin Twist (page 37) The sisters are exactly the same size — there is no difference except that one is digitally copied and placed further away than the other. This illusion is mainly caused by the strong perspective impression of the corridor. It is related to Ponzo illusion.

Squares Quandary (page 38) Sometimes, orientation changes the perception of size! The two quadrilateral shapes are actually squares identical in size. The one on the right appears different and larger only because it has been rotated through 45 degrees.

Arches (page 39) Yes, the curved lines meet correctly.

Dice Dilemma (page 40) Though the central gray round dot of the furthest dice seems much larger, both gray dots are exactly the same size.

Fraser Spiral (page 41) Although the overlapping dark arc segments appear to form a spiral, in reality they are just aligned in a series of concentric circles. This optical illusion is named the Fraser spiral illusion, after the Scottish physician and psychologist James Fraser, who first described it.

Chinese T (page 42) Although the rods appear to be of the same length, the black rod is 12 per cent longer than the white one.

Eiffel Tower (page 43) Neither. This is a photograph of the kind that people often take when visiting historical monuments such as the Tower of Pisa, the Pyramids and the Taj Mahal. The Eiffel Tower in this vintage photograph is in the far background, and the man is near the camera holding his arm up over nothing. The camera is positioned so that these two elements are made to appear as though they were touching. As the image is presented in a two-dimensional plane, the tower seems undersized.

Goldfish (page 44) Both are the same size. The bottom fish seems larger because of its proximity to the glass edge, which makes it appear more tightly confined.

Coaxial Rings (page 45) Though the patterned circles seem to be off-center and even to have curvatures that telescope into one another, they are perfectly circular and have a common center. Moreover, the rings will seem to counter-rotate when you approach or move away from the picture while concentrating on its center.

Brush Illusion (page 46) In this picture, the two curved strokes are identical, although the lower one (Fig. B) appears to be larger. This cognitive illusion is mainly due to our prior assumptions regarding perspective.

Divergent Bands (page 47) All the columns, black and white, are perfectly parallel to each other.

Planisphere Center (page 48) Chances are that you have answered dot B, but it is dot A that is actually the center of the planisphere.

Disrupted Lines (page 49) No, but you have to take a closer look at the pattern in order to realize it is composed only of short intermittent segments.

Distorted Wallpaper (page 50) Though they appear to be sloped, the columns of stacked white and black patterns are perfectly parallel to each other.

Tilting Effect (page 51) Though they appear to tilt, the vertical and horizontal sets of gray lines are straight and perfectly perpendicular to each other.

Bed Length (page 52) You have probably answered bed C, but the correct answer is bed B (see picture). Estimating the dimension of objects on paper is quite different from doing it in real three-dimensional life!

Connected Lines (page 53) The segments of each line are perfectly straight and collinear to each other. Strangely, the segment of line AB entering from A (on the left) does not appear to be in alignment with the whole line. The same applies to line CD. The segment entering from D (on the right) does not seem to be aligned with the rest.

Inner Squares (page 54) The inner square B appears larger, yet both squares are the same size. The visual effect is the result of the contrast in size of the surrounding squares. This illusion was described by the Japanese psychologist Torao Obonai.

Perfect Circle (page 55) Shape distortion can occur when contrasting objects are nearby. Yes, it is a perfect circle, though the points of the stars have the effect of making the circle appear slightly flat.

Wobbly Walls? (page 56) The walls are perfect parallelograms and both surfaces are identical in shape and size, even though they look very different!

Aligned Balls (page 57) The lines in the background may confuse or break the visual linear appearance of the dots, yet they are perfectly collinear and parallel to each other.

Ball Distance (page 58) We are influenced by the position of the shadow of the dark gray ball on the left. This ball appears to be floating in the foreground, while the bright ball is behind and to the right in the background. We see that both balls are equal in size, but depth cues tell us that the second ball is further away and therefore must be larger.

Fit the Shapes (page 59) No, not one can be fitted into another!

Parallel Lines (page 60) Even though they seem to bulge inwards, they are straight and parallel to each other. This distortion illusion is caused by the circle in the background.

Parallel Lines 2 (page 61) No, they are straight and parallel to each other. This distortion illusion is produced by the cross in the background.

Middle Point (page 62) Dot C. Obviously the surface of the vase above dot C is considerably larger than the surface below it. This discrepancy tends to confuse our mind and make accurate distance estimation difficult.

Shifting Alignment (page 63) Most readers will answer yes, but the actual answer is no. The alignment of dark balls will shift ball B because it is larger than the distance that separates balls A and B. This is an interactive adaptation of Müller-Lyer illusion.

Straw Alignment (page 64) Yes, the black diagonals on the straws are collinear to each other (see the picture). This illusion is related to Poggendorff illusion.

Misaligned Edges (page 65) The edge of the lower shelf on the left is a continuation of the edge of the single shelf (see the picture).

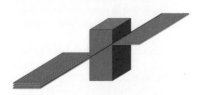

Interspace Poles (page 66) All the interspaces between the poles are exactly the same width.

Pisa Tower (page 67) The painting on the right. See picture.

Concentric Squares (page 68) Yes, they are. Curiously, the illusion effect vanishes when the image is reduced or seen from a distance.

Distorted Checkerboard (page 69) No, they are perfectly straight and at right angles.

Aligned SZ Squares (page 70) Though the upper chequered surface appears to wave, and the lower one seems to shrink towards its center, all the squares are perfectly straight and aligned.

Snake Charmer (page 71) No, the ropes are straight and parallel to each other. It is the pattern of tilted elements inside the ropes that generates these interesting curvature effects.

Women Divers (page 72) The upper diver appears to be taller than the lower one, despite the fact that both are exactly the same height. Size perception depends strongly on the eye's interpretation of depth cues. Our visual system naturally compensates for size estimations according to perspective: if two objects have the same visual size but one is farther away, the more distant object is perceived as larger.

Tire Size (page 73) Eighty per cent of people polled to say the farthest line (B) is longer, but in fact it is shorter than the closest one (A). There are two factors that strongly influence the brain to arrive at the wrong answer: the context and the distance.

Distorted Squares (page 74) The geometric shapes look like distorted squares of different sizes, but in fact they are all the same size and are perfectly right-angled squares. The visual distortion is caused by the radial spokes in the background which intersect the sides of the squares at an obtuse angle, giving the viewer the impression there is some sort of perspective.

Müller-Lyer Variant (page 75) Both are the same length. This is a clever variation of Müller-Lyer illusion, a size-consistency illusion.

Crayon Distortion (page 76) Though the inner and outer border of the central ring seem off-center and distorted, they are perfect concentric circles.

AMBIGUOUS AND IMPOSSIBLE FIGURES:
SOLUTIONS

Strange Dogs (page 77) Don't try to count them — this is just a canine impossible figure!

Impossible Bars (page 78) This is an impossible figure as the side of one plank becomes the side of another. The correct representation should be as shown in the drawing here.

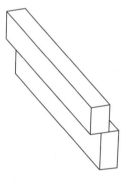

Lego Structure (page 79) No — this is an impossible structure that can exist only on paper!

Mystery Woman (page 80) You can see her from behind or, if you hide the shaded arm with a pencil as shown in the example (or with any other oblong object), you will see her face on. This demonstrates that the same picture can take on new meaning according to the context within which it is seen.

How Many Prongs (page 81) This is a kind of 'undecidable figure'. The fork appears to have four prongs at one end which then mysteriously transform into three prongs at the other end.

Barking Dog (page 81) A cat (turn the page upside down).

Cat Shadow (page 82) The real cat is shown upside-down, with its shadow appearing above.

Reversible Head (page 83) Turn the page upside-down and you will see a police officer. This is a topsy-turvy caricature by (yes, by) Lord Kitchener.

Silverplate Face (page 84) To see him turn the page 90 degrees anti-clockwise.

Staircase to Nowhere (page 85) The platform and stair form an impossible continuous loop. The girl could climb the stairs forever and never get any higher.

Face Illusion (page 86) The trees and the branches define the contour and eyes of a woman's face, while the boat and the sail are her nose and her lips.

Elephants' Ball (page 87) You are seeing more legs than you should, because the legs that ought to appear have been erased and moved over to the side, filling the interspaces.

Cubic Structure (page 88) The way this structure is drawn means you can look up at one man, while looking down at the other one!

Impossible Box (page 89) No, you can't. The box and the play blocks cannot exist in the real world — if you look closely, you can clearly see that they are impossible objects.

Piranesi Puzzle (page 90) In terms of perspective, the arch — which is in the background, emphasized with a bold dark outline — is wrongly aligned with the lower part of the architectural structure in the foreground, also emphasized with a bold dark outline.

Hearn Illusionist (page 91) The scene on stage looks like the illusionist's face. So, there are in all eight people, illusionist included.

Bear Seal (page 92) Both! This is an ambiguous optical illusion showing a polar bear crawling out of a water hole in the ice and a seal lying on the ice facing to the left.

Three Structures (page 93) All of them!

Double Face (page 94) This is a puzzling example of an ambiguous illustration that has a double meaning: you can see one face front-view and/or two profiles. There are actually two possible visual interpretations of depth: you may see one face behind the candlestick or two profiles in front of the candlestick.

Ambivalent Terrace (page 95) There are two possible ways to perceive the image: from below (fig. a) or from above (fig. b).

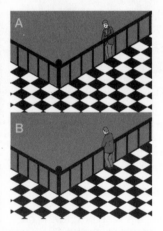

Screws and Washers (page 96) The screws and washers cannot fit together because they are impossible objects. Each item is drawn with two contradictory perspectives.

Impossible Devices (page 97) None of them could exist in real life.

Cubic Structure (page 98) Because you cannot set the cubes either flat or vertically.

Labyrinth (page 99) No, because it is an ambiguous impossible object. In fact, when you stare at the wire structure for a while, it seems to flip its orientation between two possible visual interpretations. Moreover, the structure is impossible because the top and the bottom of the structure are not congruent.

Impossible Trees (page 100) None of them, because they are impossible figures: the higher part of their trunk is not congruent with their respective lower part. In fact, they are shifted one place to the left.

Impossible Stairs (page 101) The steps gradually turn into holes in the pavement.

Interlaced Rings (page 102) To convince yourself that this is an impossible construction, just follow the path of each ring with your finger. You will discover that the inside of the rings becomes the outside, and vice versa.

Stairs to Heaven (page 103) Because the risers (vertical faces) and treads (top surfaces) of the steps are blended together.

Seal Toucan (page 104) With just a simple turn of the wrist the seal transforms into a toucan!

Ambivalent Chair (page 105) From the front — but the shadow of the rungs on the seat can easily mislead your sense of the perspective!

Impossible Wrapping (page 106) This crate is a derivative of Escher's cube — it cannot be wrapped because it is an impossible object.

Hidden Birds (page 107) You can see either four chirping baby chicks in one nest and a mother bird, or four birds sitting in their respective nests and one standing on a branch (see picture).

Paradoxical Lego Structure (page 108) No, this is a Lego structure that no one could ever build.

Emerging Face (page 109) If you look at the center of this photograph for a while a face will emerge.

Impossible Band (page 110) Though the straight arms of the structure are perfectly aligned, the circular ends, in defiance of every law of perspective, are perpendicular to each other.

Origami Magic (page 111) No, it is just an impossible paper folding performance.

Perplexing Architecture (page 112) The upper and lower sections of the building seem to share a common side, but they are actually a collage of two contrasting points of view of the same palace (the Palazzo Reale in Genoa, Italy). The two façades with the portals seem unexpectedly to lean forwards or backwards depending on your angle of view.

Ambiguous Cubes (page 113) Some people are able to perceive a medium-sized cube floating in front of the larger cube. If you turn the picture upside-down, you may see the medium cube resting in the back corner of three perpendicular adjoining planes; or you may see a large cube with a corner cube cut out. The two smallest shapes that accompany the largest and medium cubes can be seen as two solid cubes or just as two small perpendicular adjoining planes.

Arcade People (page 114) The top and bottom parts of the arcade are at different angles (the top part is linear while at the bottom there is a series of angular protruding structures).

Peacock (page 115) Turn the picture upside down to find the man.

Three Women (page 116) Standing between the two women facing each other there is a third woman wearing a black dress.

Something Looms (page 117) Look at the picture from a distance and you will discover a skull.

Earth Woman (page 118) You may perceive a woman's face. Three continents — Europe, Asia and Africa — form her hair, and her earring is the island of Madagascar. Published as a postcard, this work by James Montgomery Flagg from 1913 is called *Map of the World*.

Penrose Stairs (page 119) If they perform a continuous loop on this staircase, the man wearing the white sweater will go upstairs forever and never get any higher, while the man with the dark sweater will go downstairs forever and never get any lower. But this is clearly impossible in the real three-dimensional world! This picture, created by G. Sarcone, is a variant of an impossible construction called the 'Penrose stairs'.

Mirror Devil (page 120) About evil things! In fact, the two mirrored feminine figures form a laughing devil's face (see the picture from a distance).

Camouflage Stripes (page 121) A camouflaged World War II torpedo boat. Strongly contrasting stripes make accurate observation from a distance virtually impossible, as demonstrated by this camouflaged boat.

Perpetual Motion (page 122) No, because it is a kind of visual illusion called an impossible structure. This realistic but paradoxical artwork by the Japanese artist Mitsumasa Anno is titled *The Myth of Sisyphus*.

Vasarely Structure (page 123) The volume represents both an ambiguous structure and an impossible structure. It can actually be seen as a protruding or as a caved-in volume. This picture is named after Victor Vasarely who created a series of similar paintings.

Magnetic Eyes (page 124) Curiously enough, from whichever point you look at the woman, she seems to be insistently gazing at you! Actually, when we see perfectly round pupils we understand that the eyes are looking at us.

Ambiguous Car (page 125) The car can be seen simultaneously from the front, side or back.

Sea Legs (page 126) The figures and the background of the picture are blended together so that the lower part of the sailors' legs has shifted between the interspace of the upper part of the legs.

Strange Cylinders (page 127) The spiraling structures are impossible structures; that is, they can be designed on paper or on any other two-dimensional surface, but cannot be constructed in the three-dimensional world.

Impossible Vault (page 128) No, because the lower part of the reinforced door seems to open both outwards and inwards!

Acrobat Girl (page 129) The acrobat is performing on an impossible ceiling-hung structure (examine carefully the orientation of the structure and the rung held by the acrobat).

Impossible Die (page 130) No one can throw such a die — it can exist only in your imagination, because the length and width of the adjacent faces do not coincide. This impossible figure seems consistent but can only be depicted on paper.

Tennis (page 131) The ground of the tennis court can be interpreted with two contradictory perspectives: it is hard to distinguish where the normal view ends and the upside-down view begins!

Mystery House (page 132) The door is open simultaneously

outwards and inwards. The roof ends in another direction in relation to the house; and the leaves near the entry steps are ambiguous, since we cannot say if they lie on the ground or on the branches of the trees.

Impossible Bicycle (page 133) No, it cannot roll because it is an impossible object. If you observe the 'wheel' carefully you will notice that it is both a flat hexagon and a solid cube.

Odd Pentagon (page 134) Perspectively speaking, the Z-shaped board intersects the pentagon at three impossible points.

Missing Bottle (page 135) The bottle is concealed between the two glasses. The other oddity is that it is impossible to say if the branched candlestick has two or three sticks.

A Question of Columns (page 136) The columns seem to be either cylindrical or rectangular; the boy's cart has an impossible shape; the upper part of the bird fountain appears to be in front of the column, while the lower part is behind; the stairs seem to descend in a continuous loop; and the water jet passes through the banister.

Confusing Colanders (page 137) The top colander appears to be concave and the bottom one appears convex, unless you turn the page upside-down and then your perception reverses! Depending on your point of view —

the way you perceive the direction from which the light falls — the same object may appear concave or convex.

Up or Down (page 138) The man is neither descending nor ascending, because the drawing depicts an impossible staircase. Although the staircase is conceptually impossible, this is not apparent to many people!

Globes (page 139) Both of these visual interpretations are possible as this is an undecidable figure.

Reader (page 140) This is a form of impossible figure. The lower and upper part of the man seem to face in different directions.

Cubic Structure (page 141) It is just an impossible structure. This picture, called Multi-link Cubes, was created by Vicente Meavilla Seguí.

Henry VIII and Anne of Cleves (page 142) Turn the picture upside-down and you will discover how ugly his wife was reputed to be! The drawing was inspired by a caricature by English artist Rex Whistler (1905–44).

Mountain Magic (page 143) A sleeping face is embedded in the mountain.

Ratting Cat (page 144) This is a kind of reversible figure — the face of the rat is blended with the nose of the cat.

Masked Lovers (page 145) Most people who see the picture for the first time do not notice that it is actually both: a woman on the left who kisses a man on the right. This optical illusion was presented to the public by the authors of this book at the 2011 Best Illusion of the Year Contest, held at the Philharmonic Center for the Arts in Naples, Florida.

Old Young Man (page 146) To see him, turn the picture upside-down. The drawing was inspired by a caricature by English artist Rex Whistler (1905–44).

Reverse Side Painting (page 147) As an amusement, the canvas was painted by the Flemish artist Cornelius Gijsbrecht to resemble the back of a painting, complete with price tag! One of the pleasures of this painting is in representing and seeing what normally is not seen. The technique that involves realistic imagery in order to create the illusion that the depicted objects appear in three dimensions is called trompe-l'oeil.

BRIGHTNESS AND MOVEMENT ILLUSIONS:
SOLUTIONS

Scintillating Discs (page 148) Although they are static, the central discs of the sun-like shapes appear to scintillate and rotate.

Christmas Lights (page 149) The illusion is caused by the alternation of small dark strokes with the white background. Also, the rapid movement of the eyes produces repeated afterimages that create the illusion of motion.

Map Illusion (page 150) Although the land in the map seems slightly shaded, it does not contain any gray shade at all. The illusion that it does is produced by the contrasting gray shades used to distinguish the boundaries of the continents and seas. This illusion, called the 'mapmaker color illusion', was used by early cartographers to differentiate one country from another.

Chaotic Texture (page 151) Small circles seem to appear and fade as the eye moves over them! This occurs because our visual system is searching for the best interpretation of this unorganized pattern.

Camouflaged Balls (page 152) There are 24 balls (see picture).

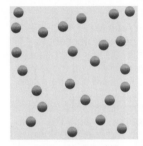

Spinning Vortex (page 153) The dots on the spirals appear to vibrate and twinkle, but they are obviously still. This effect is produced by heavy brightness contrasts and rapid random eye movements called microsaccades.

Square Composition (page 154) The two arrangements are made up with the same gray-shaded squares, but the visual effect is quite different with the outlines present. In A, the squares seem distorted and shiny, whereas in B some have haloed effects.

Vibrating Discs (page 155) The apparent movement comes from the repetition of bright and dark decorative elements.

Gray-shaded Squares (page 156) Though the second column of squares appears darker than the first one, all the squares are exactly the same shade. This is a variant of the Craik-O'Brien-Cornsweet illusion.

Rotation Arcs (page 157) The rings are perfectly concentric, though they appear to cross over each other. When you move your head the rings will counter-rotate.

Gray Cross (page 158) All the four spots have exactly the same brightness and hue. The illusion due to an effect known as the simultaneous brightness contrast effect.

Stubbs Illusion (page 159) When you look at the center of the image the black central smudge seems to expand. When you move your head away the smudge will seem to shrink. This illusion, based on the Stubbs illusion, uses dynamic luminance-gradient effects.

Moving Smudges (page 160) As you move your eyes around the picture the smudges will start to move slightly and float.

Madonna Afterimage (page 161) An aura surrounding a feminine face will slowly appear in your mind and then vanish. This illusion is an afterimage effect.

Disappearing Eye (page 162) You might find the eye completely disappears!

Moving Rays (page 163) You may perceive a shimmering swirl around the center of the picture and a swarming effect around the black disc. You may also see colors.

Misleading Stripes (page 164) Rectangles A and B have exactly the same brightness and width.

Celtic Patterns (page 165) The curvilinear shapes are all of the same shade. This illusion is related to the Benussi ring illusion and is mainly due to the lateral inhibition of our visual system.

Neon Brightness (page 166) You may see intermittent dark smudges on the stripes but this is an illusion caused by 'lateral inhibition', which enhances the contrast of the outline of an object.

White Effect (page 167) Though the two sets of gray vertical bars appear different, they are perfectly identical in shade and color. This illusion is called 'White's illusion' or 'achromatic Munker effect'.

Ehrenstein Figure (page 168) You may perceive bright discs even though there are no edges to define them. These virtual circles are a construct of your mind!

Rotating Spirals (page 169) You may see one large illusionary spiral, though in reality there is just a series of concentric circles. The spiral-like pattern seems to rotate clockwise slightly, although the image is perfectly static.

Cat Sofa (page 170) You might be surprised by the answer: stripe C is the same. This is the result of the simultaneous brightness contrast effect.

Concentric Swarming (page 171) You may perceive a continuous rotating, vibrating effect. Brightness contrasts are responsible for this optical effect.

Nureyev Illusion (page 172) If you look at the horizontal pattern in the shape representing a dancer, you may notice that it appears to move relative to the vertical pattern in the surround. This diagram was adapted from a design created by the Japanese artist Hajime Ouchi.

Hermann Grid (page 173) The gray spots appear as a result of visual overstimulation caused by successive afterimage effects. If you stare at one gray spot it will disappear; if you tilt the image by 45 degrees or look at the figure from different distances all the gray spots will disappear at once!

Squares of Confusion (page 174) The gray designs will seem to slightly float and move over the dark background. Most people believe there are two or three types of pattern, but in fact there is only one; the floating patterns look different because the regularity of their shape is disturbed by the background.

Tonal Illusion (page 175) The answer is ball C, even if it seems darker than ball A. This is a simultaneous lightness contrast effect.

Levitating Ball (page 176) Of course the picture is static. Some scientists think that the illusion of motion is caused by unconscious random eye movements (saccades). This picture was adapted from a design created by Japanese artist Hajime Ouchi.

Explosion (page 177) The effects of this illusion are analogous to those of the Ouchi illusions on pages 172 and 176, with an extra dynamic effect — the blurred drops seem to expand when you move your head toward the image.

Pulsating Pattern (page 178) While you stare at the image, the pattern not only seems to pulsate but you may also see a range of dark spots alternately appearing and disappearing within the central gray disc. Furthermore, the gray disc seems to float slightly.

Moving Arcs (page 179) The horizontal patterned bands seem to move to and fro.

Fairies (page 180) The wings of the seated fairy in the negative seem much darker than those in the first shot, but in fact they are identical in shape and brightness in both plates. Artists well know that an object with a standard brightness can be perceived as darker or lighter according to the context in which it is seen.

Moving Lines (page 181) The vertical lines will start to move slightly! This illusion works best when seen with peripheral vision.

Illusory Squares and Discs (page 182) The blank spaces at the intersections of the grid are not seen as empty, but as illusory bright circles or squares. The blank spaces crossed by X's are however perceived as squares, because the arms of each X define the 4 angles of a square. These illusory figures depend on regular 'gaps' in the grid lines.

Brightness and Contrast Bars (page 183) The gray bar on the contrasted background is the same shade throughout. Therefore, the answer is bar A. This illusion that the tone deepens along the bar is based on the simultaneous color brightness effect.

Grid Illusion (page 184) You may see ghost dark spots appear at the intersection of the bars. You may also perceive subjective translucent rings that actually do not exist. This illusion combines the Lingelbach grid effect with the VanTujl neon illusion.

Rotating Patterns (page 185) The three circular patterns will start to counter-rotate! Some regular concentric objects appear to rotate when we approach or move back from them. Poor integration of motion signals in our brain may be one of the causes of this rotation illusion.

Spots or Not? (page 186) The gray spots set on the darker background appear lighter than the gray spots on the clearer background, but all are identical in shade and brightness! This visual phenomenon is simultaneous brightness contrast.

Follow My Eyes (page 187)
1. The concentric circles appear to rotate in opposite directions!
2. The concentric circles seem to expand or shrink, like the aperture of a camera, depending on the swinging direction you give to the picture.

Floating Balls (page 188) The seven bright circular patches should start to float and to rotate slightly. This motion or peripheral drift illusion is made with overlaying patterns generated with a flow direction. In fact, the background and the circular patches counter-rotate, the effect being determined by the contrasting black and white offsets.

Radial Pulses (page 189) The alignments of white discs seem to pulse like the runway lights of an aerodrome.

Black Patches (page 190) No, the black patches are solid geometric shapes, they aren't blurred at all! If you sweep your gaze around the picture you may see the patches move. You may also perceive colors on the background.

Vasarely Adaptation (page 191) You may perceive brighter diagonals, but in fact they do not exist!

Disappearing Face (page 192) The face will gradually disappear. This is because, viewed with a steady gaze, the slight shade difference between dark and clear gray is a poor stimulus for sustaining visual perception. Eye movement will trigger the reappearance of the face.

VISUAL AND COGNITIVE TESTS:
SOLUTIONS

Tool Search
There are 28 tools in total, including 19 white tools on a black background and 9 black tools on a white background.

Someone in the Sunset (page 194) It's Marilyn Monroe (see the picture from a distance)

Hidden Animal (page 195) To find it, turn the page upside down and look at the picture from a distance. You should see the deer 'pop' out.

Black and White Confusion (page 196) A black and white spotted cat lying on a black and white cowskin rug (see the picture). Figure and ground have been deliberately obscured to challenge the brain and illustrate the importance of prior experience to discern the meaning of an image.

Find the Cross (page 197) See the picture.

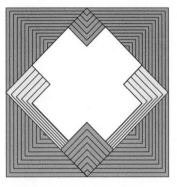

Ant Army (page 198) You probably thought there were more white ants, but there are actually equal numbers of ants. The ant square formation is perfectly straight.

William Tell Illusion (page 199) In this figure-ground illusion it is possible to perceive eight arrows (see the picture).

Old Swiss Mill (page 200) There is a donkey's head in the bottom right-hand corner of the picture beneath the tree roots. You can also perceive a large cat in the trees on the top left-hand side, and some human faces in the rocks. A bear, a lion, a snake, a mule and a dog are just a few of the other surprises hidden in the artwork.

Clock Test (page 201) Batch number 2.

Hidden in a Horse (page 202) Have a look at the large white spot on the head of the horse and you will find the silhouette of her boyfriend.

Tricky Calculator (page 203) Chances are that you answered 5,000 instead of 4,100! Tricky isn't it?

Mystery Photo (page 204) If you rotate the picture 90 degrees clockwise, you will see a nice little puppy taking a nap!

Dartboard Doubt (page 205) The area of the outer dark ring is the same as the inner clear disc.

Broken Dish (page 206) If you concentrate hard enough, after some time it will seem that the broken piece of the dish rejoins the rest. At least the outer black rim should appear as a perfect non-broken circle.

Panda Puzzle (page 207) The silhouette of the panda cub is amid the weeds on the right side of mother panda, while the face of her companion is outlined by the flowers and leaves at her left side.

Dots to Squares (page 208). See the picture for the solution.

Snap-hooks (page 209) Open three snap-hooks of one chain portion. With these, link the other four chain portions together.

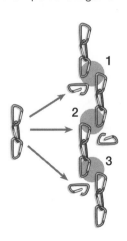

Complete the Drawing (page 210) See the picture. Our expectations always affect perception and influence how we understand our world.

Rorschach Test (page 211) Turn the page 90 degrees clockwise and you will discover a walking black bear cub and his reflection in the water.

Unbroken Line (page 212) See the picture. Such a drawing is called a unicursal curve — one that you get when you put your pen on the paper and draw until you get back to the starting point. As you draw, your mark can intersect itself.

Shape Shading (page 213) The number of concave and convex zones changes, since the convexity or concavity of a surface depends on the perceived direction of the shade.

Coffee Beans (page 214) See picture.

Glass Experiment (page 215) It is real! You can reproduce this installation by using two aligned glasses and a bright bicolor background. You will obtain the optical effect shown on the picture only when both glasses are full of water (or vodka, if you prefer).

Gears (page 216) Because the following items are 'impossible', drawn by matching together two or more different points of view of the same object, or by extending and blending together the perspective of one object with that of another one. (From left to right): 1. the belt; 2. the teeth of the gear wheels; 3.

the axis of the belt wheels; 4. the axle that passes through the two vertical metal pieces. The other incongruities are shown in the picture.

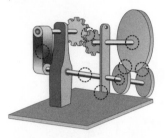

Psychedelic Puzzle (page 217) The concentric sets of dots create this psychedelic Mona Lisa. The picture is best viewed from a distance.

Find the Animal (page 218) A swimming dolphin (picture courtesy of coolbubble.com).

Caught in a Loop (page 219) Both! Try this experiment yourself with a piece of string.

Find the Arrows (page 220) There are 48 arrows in all, though two sets are not easy to perceive (see A and B). This is a figure-ground perceptual illusion based on the fact that we tend to perceive a figure that stands out from the background.

Path Problem 1 (page 221) See the picture.

Halloween Popcorn (page 222) At least seven! See the picture.

Path Problem 2 (page 223) See the picture.

Hidden Squares (page 228) There are 13 perfect squares in the picture! Did you manage to discover all of them? (See the picture.)

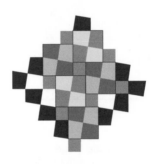

Hidden Elephants (page 224) The elephants appear in or partly in the following squares: A2, H3, F6 and D9.

Handprint Illusion (page 225) A gorilla is visible — see the picture.

Tiger Face (page 226) The camouflaged profile of the child is on the tiger's cheek.

Hidden Girl (page 227) You can detect the face of a smiling young woman camouflaged under the bridge (see the picture from a distance).

Hidden Zebra (page 229) See the picture. To see the third zebra within the grass you have to turn the picture upside-down.

Multiple Babies (page 230) There are seven distinct babies (three babies' heads with interchangeable bodies).

Hidden Discs (page 231) First-time viewers do not usually see the four circles segmented from the background (see the picture).

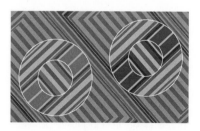

Magic Pin (page 232) Either!

Impossible Paths (page 233) See the picture.

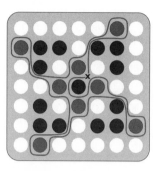

Making Contact (page 234) Slowly draw the image closer to your nose and at a certain point the fingers will touch each other.

Sailor Thoughts (page 235) Turn the picture upside-down and you will discover the face of a woman.

Old and Young (page 236) If you observe the picture carefully, you will notice that the grandmother's nose is the girl's chin; her mouth is the girl's necklace, and her eye is the girl's ear! This old illusion shows how our visual system tends to group features based upon what we expect to see.

Blivet Structure (page 237) Either! This is a kind of 'undecidable monument'.

Shadow (page 238) It is just the shadow of a person's left hand. Western people are not used to imagining blank or empty spaces as figures. We always tend to give meaning to black, solid figures, ignoring the white, blank interspaces that surround them.

The Long View (page 239) The trick lies in the four mirrors concealed inside the telescope and in the table, as you can see from the picture.

Rabbit Hunter (page 240) The man is outlined by the branches of the tree on the left, while the rabbit is outlined by the branches of two trees on the right. This is an intriguing advertisement label for the toy manufacturer Jacob Shaffer, printed in 1866.

Herd of Elephants (page 241) There are 13 elephants: 12 elephants confounded in multiple bodies and a single one. In Japan, figures with multiple or with composite bodies are part of the artistic tradition.

Marbles Test (page 242) There are three white-and-gray marbles located in C2, F4, and G2. This test has been created by psychologists to demonstrate that in visual perception, search is very difficult when you have to find an object with a combination of two of the same attributes (here colors), than with more complex attributes such as color and form.

Bewildered Hunter (page 243) In the picture you may find: two hunters in the trees and a face by the branches; three deer, one in the cave and two in front of the hunter next to each other; a face looking up in the lower right-hand corner; a cat and tiger next to each other just under the hunter; a black dog next to the first deer; two faces above the water, one with a long nose; a couple of human faces in the clouds; and an eagle next to the bear to the right.

Fox Puzzle (page 244) In this picture puzzle you can find: the horse's head turned toward you, between the trees, to the left of the fox's head; the lamb seated in the lower left-hand corner, its head in the tree trunk; and the large head of the wild boar between the horse's legs, coming towards you. The men's and women's profiles are outlined by the trees and leaves (there are at least 34 human faces!)

Ambiguous Cheese (page 245) It is an ambiguous picture: if you tilt the picture 90 degrees clockwise, you will see a piece of cheese under a cheese dish cover. But if you tilt the picture 90 degrees anticlockwise, you will see a cheese with a triangular piece carved out.

Rectangle Square (page 246) Most people will answer b) rectangle, instead of the correct solution: c) square.

Frankenstein's Dream (page 247) When you see the picture close-up, the fine details dominate (Frankenstein), but when you observe it from a distance, the larger, more blurred tones become more coherent and, in this case, a beautiful woman appears (Marilyn Monroe).

Gestalt Test (page 248) You may see a man riding a horse. According to the Gestalt psychology, we tend to enclose a space by completing a contour and ignoring gaps in the figure, and to organize a figure into a symmetrical, simple and regular composition.

Cow Drinking (page 249) Answer: cows drink water!

Kersten Ball (page 250) The balls appear to rest on the surface and recede in the upper picture, while in the lower picture they seem to rise above the surface and to be aligned with the second checkered row. But the only difference between the two pictures is the position of the cast shadows. This shadow illusion is called Kersten's ball illusion.

Ambiguous Cubes (page 251) When the picture is turned upside-down, the protruding cube-cornered structure transforms into a cubic hollowed-out structure.

Multiple Horses (page 252) It is possible to simultaneously perceive two galloping horses and two bucking horses, as demonstrated in the two boxed pictures. This example of horses with interchangeable bodies is a modern rendering of an artwork by an unknown Safavid artist of the 15th century.

Invisible Woman (page 253) It is just your imagination. Even though there are no lines to form a regular solid figure your brain re-creates the contours of a woman from the 'gaps'.

Talking Cups (page 254) The outline of the first cup in the background profiles the faces of two frowning people. In the second cup, we can see that they are now sticking out their tongues at each other; and finally, in the third cup, they laugh.

Reversed Faces (page 255) When the face of the second boy is seen right side up it appears quite monstrous, because he has his mouth and eyes inverted. Strangely, he doesn't appear so weird when he is upside down!

How Many Triangles (page 256) There are in all 11 triangles: three small white triangles, three small gray triangles, three large gray triangles, and two illusory bright triangles (see picture).

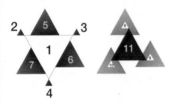

Perceptual Set (page 257) A man taking off his hat. 'Perceptual set' is a predisposition to perceive something in relation to prior perceptual experiences.

Shapes Puzzle (page 258) The shape A! (See the picture.)

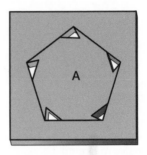

Cheese Vision (page 259) You have probably answered piece of cheese b). Wrong! The correct answer is piece of cheese a).

Seeing Double (page 260) The eyes and mouth of the woman have been duplicated. Our mind fails to recognize and fuse doubled-up features, so the woman's face appears unstable and wobbly. If you glance at her out of the corner of your eye, you probably won't notice her double imaging.

Follow Your Star (page 261) See the picture.

Rectangle Puzzle (page 16) The top rectangle is the same as the second one in shape and size, though the former appears to be slimmer and longer than the latter.

Convergent Alignments (page 17) The two vertical alignments of black and white segments are perfectly parallel to each other.

Delboeuf Illusion (page 18) All the discs are exactly the same size.

Compare the Elephants (page 19) Neither is heavier, because the balance in the picture is perfectly level, even though it seems to tilt to the right. The visual distortion is induced by the contrast between the inset patterns of tilted lines and the outlines of the rectangles that represent the balance.

The Ames Room (page 20) The boy appears to be a giant because of the particular spatial configuration of the room. The room looks cubic when seen from a particular viewpoint, however its true shape is trapezoidal. This mistaken shape makes it look as though people grow or shrink as they move from one corner of the room to another. Such perspectival illusion rooms are called 'Ames rooms' after the US ophthalmologist A. Ames.

Distorted Squares (page 21) Ninety-nine per cent of people say only square B seems distorted; the reality is that square A is distorted (concave) while square B is not.

Distorted Frame (page 22) Yes, they are!

Spiralling Discs (page 23) You may see a continuous spiral. However, there isn't any spiral at all, because the main disc is composed only of a series of superimposed white and black discs.

Pills Series (page 24) Yes, the horizontal lines are perfectly parallel to each other.

Five Cylinders (page 25) See the picture for the answer.

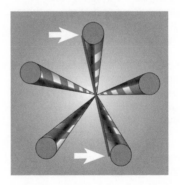

SOLUTIONS

Tolansky Curvature (page 6) Though the bottom arc (C) is perceived as having the least curvature, all the arc segments are in fact identical in curvature. Our assessment of curvature is strongly influenced by the length of the curved line.

Arrowhead Illusion (page 7) Arrow A. This illusion is related to Poggendorf illusion.

Halfway Heart (page 8) The dot is located midway, although it appears to be much lower.

Shepard Tabletop (page 9) The two tabletops are identical in size and shape. If you don't believe it, trace them out and compare them. This illusion is based on Shepard's tables illusion.

Straight — or not? (page 10) The checkered frames are perfectly straight! The small white and black squares create layouts of subliminal oblique lines which interfere with the orthogonal outlines of the frames, creating the illusion of bulging. If you observe the picture with half-closed eyes, you can perceive these subliminal oblique lines. This is a neat version of the Zöllner illusion.

Divergent Crosses (page 11) The columns are perfectly parallel to each other. This illusion is related to Zöllner illusion.

Wider or Taller (page 12) The polo shirt is wider, though that's hard to believe. Scientists have long known that the subjective perception of the length of the same object (line, shape) varies according to the way it is oriented on a plane. This visual effect was reported in the huge medieval treatise *De viribus quantitatis* written by the Italian mathematician Luca Bartolomeo de Pacioli in 1496–1508. Pacioli presented it as a geometric puzzle to point out our tendency to over-estimate vertical distances.

Bowling Ball Size (page 13) The bowling balls are actually the same size, although the ball being thrown by the player seems larger. This is a variant of Ponzo illusion, in which the angle of two converging lines in the background creates apparent depth through linear perspective.

Müller-Lyer Illusion (page 14) The correct answer is B. If you don't believe it, measure the segments for yourself!

Helicopter Lines (page 15) It looks as though the line of the upper helicopter is longest but if you measure them, you will find that the line of the lower helicopter is longer.

Landscape Length
Is the line AB as long as the line AC?

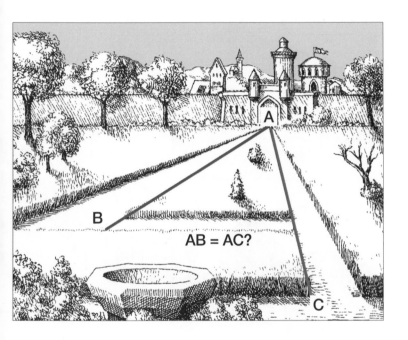

AB = AC?

Solution on page 304

R Shapes

Observe the surfaces of the three Rs. There are at least two R-shapes that are congruent (equal) — can you find them?

Solution on page 304

Las Meninas

Where is the main subject in this painting by the Spanish artist Diego Velásquez?

Solution on page 304

Gear Belt Puzzle 2

When Fred the hamster starts running, will the hand of the speedometer of the exercise device turn clockwise or counter-clockwise?

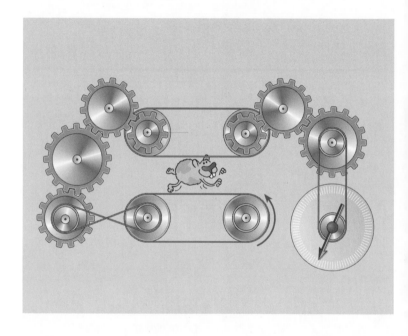

Solution on page 304

Dog or Not? (page 262) A cat curled up and taking a nap. To see it, just rotate the image counterclockwise by a quarter-turn.

Bidirectional Face (page 263) Wherever you stand, this face will follow you with its eyes! The effect is due to the structural ambiguity of the face. Our judgment of where a person is fixing their gaze is influenced by the orientation of their facial features or 'set'; in this particular case there are two distinct 'sets', but in just one image (the brow ridge and eye socket in fact face in opposing directions).

Pipes Connection Test (page 264) It is not possible to connect the supplies W, O and L to each of the three houses without crossing a pipe. In fact, the houses A and C are connected twice to the same supplier. Have a look at the diagram and you will see that three connections starting from two utility suppliers will inevitably enclose one of the houses, preventing it from being connected to at least one utility supplier.

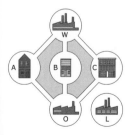

Blind Spot (page 265) By the time you reach number 4, the leprechaun will have disappeared. In our visual field there is a very large spot, called the blind spot, where the optical nerve enters the eye. This region has no photoreceptors... So, when the leprechaun enters your blind spot he naturally disappears from view.

Strange Box (page 266) This wrought-iron trunk occupies two different spatial positions. If you have difficulty seeing both, the boxes with the gray ball in them will help (see picture).

Cat-fly Blindspot (page 267) This happens when light rays reflected from the fly fall exactly on your blind spot.

Gear Belt (page 268) Device B (see picture).

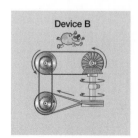

Device B

Disco Dance (page 269) There is a large face in the centre of the picture!

Buddha Among the Leaves (page 270) The face of Buddha is in C8.

Gear Belt Puzzle 2 (page 271) Counter-clockwise (see picture).

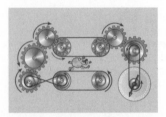

Las Meninas (page 272) No, it is not the cute little girl. The main subject is actually outside the painting! You can see the artist at work portraying the King and Queen of Spain – Philip IV and Mariana of Austria – who are the real subject of the painting. The mirror in the background reflects the King and Queen smiling at their daughter and courtiers as they pose (see picture).

R Shapes (page 273) Incredibly, the white R and the black R coincide exactly when superimposed! (See the picture.)

Landscape Length (page 274) Although 80 per cent of people think that both lines are equal, actually the line AB is much longer!